MORE
Listening
for God in
Contemporary
Fiction

THE EMMAUS READERS

Edited by
Susan M. Felch
and
Gary D. Schmidt

PARACLETE PRESS
Brewster, Massachussetts

The Emmaus Readers: More Listening for God in Contemporary Fiction

2009 First Printing

Copyright © 2009 by Susan Felch and Gary Schmidt

ISBN: 978-1-55725-544-0

Library of Congress Cataloging-in-Publication Data
  The Emmaus readers : more listening for God in contemporary
fiction / edited by Susan M. Felch and Gary D. Schmidt.
      p. cm.
   Includes bibliographical references.
   ISBN 978-1-55725-544-0
   1. Fiction—Religious aspects—Christianity. 2. God in literature.
I. Felch, Susan M., 1951- II. Schmidt, Gary D.
   PN3351.E46 2009
   809.3'93823--dc22
                                        2009000277

10 9 8 7 6 5 4 3 2 1

Published by Paraclete Press
Brewster, Massachusetts
www.paracletepress.com
Printed in the United States of America

For Jim and Shirley Weimer
and for Michele and Ryan,
with thanks for the ways you have helped me pay attention.

—S.M.F.

For Larry and Pat Perron,
with thanks for the story you tell.

—G.D.S.

Contents

Introduction

Having been together for several years now as the Emmaus Readers, it seems to us reasonable and just to offer some observations on Life Within a Book Club—which we now give here, with humility, recognizing that the experiences of book clubs will differ and that ours may be more than slightly affected by the long, gray winters of Michigan that end with the last frosts in the final week of May and pick up again with the first drifty snow that falls on golden September leaves. In such a cold, we here in Michigan tend to cling to our communities and to read about warm and blue places. It may be that those needs have affected both the selection of our books, and the frequency of our meetings. But, we suppose, all book clubs may similarly be seasonally adaptive, no matter in what part of the continent they find themselves. We may not be so different after all.

First observation: Everything in a book club goes better with good food and good drink. It really did not take us long to discover this. We began with bottles of water and quickly found that that would not do at all. We tried bright candy mints in small glass dishes and found that to be only marginally better. Cashews were better, but just by a bit. We now eat through most of our meetings and have introduced each other to European cheeses and spicy herbal spreads and twisted breads and berry jams and seasonal fruit and all manner of good things that start out in wicker baskets and find their way to the plates we balance beside our novel of the month. As for the nature of the drink we serve each other, we leave that discussion to those of wide latitudinal propensities.

What we have found is that there is something so absolutely right about this. Eating with one another is, after all, a communal act.

Sharing food creates the bonds and relationships that are essential to any community, and is simultaneously a celebration of the goodness and wholeness and marvelous nature of a world that can produce such good things, and of a God who is first the creator. These bonds and celebrations are not dissimilar from the bonds and celebrations that we establish in a book club, where we share the same reading, share openly and with some vulnerability our responses, share the same gladness of communal discussion, and share in thanksgiving for creativity that can produce such art.

Second observation: There are times when, as we gather to select books for the coming year, we think, How could our friend here, usually so sane and respectable, of such good opinion and sound judgment, have made such a loony suggestion as this novel? It is true, *loony* is the word that comes to mind. And how embarrassing that the usually sane friend pursues the choice, even when we try to push the book to the margins of our discussion, as if somehow once there, it might drop away to the oblivion it deserves. Still, the usually sane friend pursues the choice, until finally we yield, patting ourselves on the back for the grace and compassion we have shown in the face of this, well, looniness.

And then—and this is infallible—the book turns out to be wonderful, just the right one for the month, and perfect in the context of the other books we are discussing this year. How could we not have seen it at the time? How loony *we* were, and how glad we are that book clubs are there to teach us this truth: that at times, our own judgments may be narrow, provincial, parochial. A community such as this teaches us how wide is the world. A community such as this shows us how deep and wide is the love of God, who has invested creativity into his creation in such lavish measure.

Third observation: It is remarkable how frequently we come to meetings and, soon after the discussion about a book begins, think: How extraordinary that they are all so very wrong! Didn't they get it? Didn't they understand the words on the page? So we press our point and then discover, strangely, that others in the group think that, goodness, *we* are wrong! How can that be? We must not have expressed ourselves clearly enough, so we persist. And they do, too! As if they believe themselves to be right!

Book clubs teach us the value of multiple understandings and judgments. Or, to be blunt, they teach us humility. They teach us the value of the other and the other's perspective. They teach us to walk carefully with our opinions, and to hone those opinions, of course, so that we can speak well and precisely, but also to listen carefully to those other voices that may see things in an entirely different light. This is especially true, we've found, when the voices are soft and unaggressive. We remember that God speaks in a still, small voice—and in still, small voices.

Fourth observation: Firelight will do.

Fifth observation: There are times when one of us, at some point in the conversation, will read aloud a line or two that she has found to be remarkable, either because of its meaning, or its sound, or its visual beauty, or for the evidence of the loving hand of the writer. And as that line is being read aloud—it may be just a short line from a five hundred–page novel—but as it is read aloud, heads nod, and there are smiles all around. We all remember it. Many of us have marked it. And perhaps the line isn't crucial to the meaning of the book, and perhaps it isn't all that significant even in the context of its chapter, but we all remember it. It is the line that, Emily Dickinson would say, you would tip your hat to.

We are, at that moment, in perfect communion. We have all come to the same place, separately, and now together. Perhaps that is what great beauty is in the world to do.

Sixth observation: Decaffeinated coffee will *not* do.

Seventh observation: Living in a book club is dang hard work. Living in a book club means reading a novel that may be very long, that you have not chosen, that you may not be particularly excited about, and that you must finish in four weeks or less. Living in a book club means reading this novel in the cracks of all of your other commitments, which may be legion. Living in a book club means adjusting your schedule and schlepping across town or from one town to another sometimes late at night, knowing that there will be good food and talk, but looking through the windshield and wondering if those snowflakes are going to start coming down a whole lot harder before you get home—and they probably will.

A book club is, in some small way, a commitment to another. In that sense, book clubs have at least a tinge of that best of human qualities: selflessness. We gather to express ourselves, yes. But more, we gather to learn from each other, and to teach each other—or, to give and to receive grace from each other. Living in a book club is dang hard work, but it smacks of all good hard work that looks beyond the immediate and the self-centered.

Final observation: All of us come to a book club meeting with the recognition that we should be bringing something to it. On the one hand, this means that we are responsible to each other to bring our own understandings and observations to the group. But this means first that we have come to the books at hand whole-heartedly. It may be that art can speak to an empty heart and a closed soul. But art, if it is to truly speak, must speak to people who live in the world, who come to it with all of the baggage of their lives, and who confront that work by being fully present, by giving it the attention it deserves. Living in a book club reminds us to give a book the attention it deserves. Living in a book club reminds us to pay attention—and anything that will do that in a world that throws up lights and gee-gaws and glitz and celebrity so that we do not pay much attention is worth holding on to dearly.

The pieces that you are about to read represent the thoughts, musings, and observations of a group of readers like yourself, interested in the ways in which contemporary writers of fiction engage with the most significant spiritual questions and press us as readers to think seriously about how their art goes about that engagement. As in the first volume, the guides and discussion questions are meant to prompt and to prod and to point—they are not meant to serve as a substitute for reading the novels, nor are they meant to suggest that these are the sole ways of reading these novels. As we have written before, they are guides to thinking about these novels with spiritual eyes—meaning that they try to draw out the ways in which writers confront readers with the deepest matters of the spirit. In short, they suggest why it might be important to be paying attention.

As for the Emmaus Readers, we learn from each other that everything in this mortal life is transient. One of our readers will be moving to the Pacific Northwest within the year—and complains that the commute to Michigan would be terribly long, for which we have little sympathy. Another has committed more hours to his own writerly tasks, and we suppose, grudgingly, that we have to honor that. A theologian from Calvin Theological Seminary has joined the Readers and is represented now in this volume; we have tried not to designate him as the Token Theology Guy to whom we turn for clarification of ecclesiastical niceties, but sometimes we do. As for the rest of us, we read as we are given the grace to do so.

May you as well.

The Battle Hymn of the Republic

Mine eyes have seen the glory of the coming of the Lord;
He is trampling out the vintage where the grapes of wrath are stored;
He hath loosed the fateful lightning of his terrible swift sword;
His truth is marching on.

> Glory! Glory! Hallelujah!
> Glory! Glory! Hallelujah!
> Glory! Glory! Hallelujah!
> His truth is marching on.

I have seen him in the watchfires of a hundred circling camps;
They have builded him an altar in the evening dews and damps;
I can read his righteous sentence by the dim and flaring lamps;
His day is marching on.

He has sounded forth the trumpet that shall never sound retreat;
He is sifting out the hearts of men before his judgment seat;
O be swift, my soul to answer him; be jubilant, my feet!
Our God is marching on.

In the beauty of the lilies Christ was born across the sea,
With a glory in his bosom that transfigures you and me;
As he died to make men holy, let us die to make men free!
While God is marching on.

—*Julia Ward Howe, 1862*

PART ONE

"Mine Eyes Have Seen the Glory"

"Mine Eyes Have Seen the Glory"

A year into the Civil War, Julia Ward Howe wrote her "Battle Hymn of the Republic," which in its language and martial qualities echoes the powerful, confident rhythms of righteous anger. One side, Howe asserts, heads into war armed with God's truth—indeed, holding the terrible, swift sword of God himself. Certainly, ideals are powerful things to believe and to work toward, but Howe's narrator has seen them fulfilled: "Mine eyes have seen the glory."

But would that same narrator have come from the fields of Antietam, of Chancellorsville, of Gettysburg, of Shiloh, of Vicksburg, of Atlanta, having seen what happens when ideals clash, and still be able to sing confidently, "Glory! Glory! Hallelujah!"?

Perhaps. But what happens when ideals that we hold close and dear lead to disaster? What happens when our righteous anger leads to innocence defiled? What happens when our sure confidence leads to unexamined destructiveness? What happens to our individual ideals when, having been played out on a public stage, they lead in terrible, swift directions that we had never imagined? Or, what happens when ideals fail? What happens when the real world and the ideal world come up against each other and we come to impossible choices?

These are the questions the writers of this section ask, and their gaze is unflinching. In *March*, Geraldine Brooks pictures a man whose ideals are as lofty as the stars—but their loftiness itself creates their impossibility. In *Intuition*, Allegra Goodman examines the ideals of the scientific community and calls into question any real hope for objectivity in a world of human emotion and motivation. And in *Fieldwork*, Mischa Berlinski shows the clash of many goods—scientific and spiritual—and asks what might happen to those who feel called to enact those goods and those whose lives are touched by their attempts.

"Mine eyes have seen the glory," writes Julia Ward Howe. "Then hold on tight," these writers warn everyone else.

MARCH Geraldine Brooks

(2005)

Synopsis

March is a novel imaginatively constructed to push us
to consider carefully its two large sources: Louisa May
Alcott's *Little Women* and the diary and letters of Alcott's
father, Amos Bronson Alcott. From the first source, Brooks
draws the characters of the four March daughters and
the situation of their father being away during the Civil
War. From the second source, she draws the characters of
March and his wife, Marmee, as well as the description
of the idealism that dominated Bronson Alcott's life—and
that warred with his interest in the practical matters of the
world.

The novel begins with March as a chaplain (Bronson
Alcott was a teacher and educator, but never a chaplain)
fleeing a Union loss, helping a wounded soldier to escape,
and encountering the first of his many failures: while
crossing a river, the wounded soldier panics, and to save
himself, March kicks at the soldier, who drifts away and is
lost. Filled with remorse, March goes to an army hospital
established on an old plantation and finds that it is the
very plantation he had visited twenty years earlier. There
he had met Augustus Clement, a wealthy, noble, and high-
minded man to whom March was strongly attracted. He
had also met Grace, a slave, and fallen in love with her.
When, at her urging, he had taught another young slave to
read, he was found out and removed from the plantation,
but not before helplessly watching Grace being savagely
whipped at the orders of the high-minded Mr. Clement.

March does well as a traveling merchant, and he returns to New England a wealthy man. There he meets Marmee Day. Attracted by her abolitionist ideals, he soon marries her, and they have four daughters together. But the past—and March's own ideals—keep intruding, so that when the Civil War is declared, March heads south with the army as a chaplain. There he fails in battle and, later, fails in his duties as a chaplain when those to whom he preaches find him false and absurdly unworldly. He is reassigned to a contraband experiment—a cotton farm on which an Illinois businessman, Ethan Canning, is trying to run a for-profit business manned by former slaves who are now being paid for their labor. March arrives with all of his idealism and naiveté intact, and he fails to understand the real conditions under which they all labor.

The farm is destroyed by Confederate forces, and all of March's hopes and expectations are thwarted; to save something, he tracks the Rebels who have taken some of the freedmen, planning to sell them into slavery. But this plan, too, is thwarted. March is shot, rescued, and sent to a hospital, where he once again finds Grace, who nurses him until Marmee comes down to the hospital. Faced with the loss of his ideals, March has no desire to return home. He does so only with Grace's urging, there to regain some sense of purpose.

On the Author

Geraldine Brooks (b. 1955) grew up in a suburb outside Sydney, Australia, with an American father who had been an itinerant big band singer and an Australian mother who had been a radio announcer. A sickly and shy child, she resolved to overcome both encumbrances and entered into journalism, attending first Bethlehem College Ashfield and then the University of Sydney, as well as the graduate school of journalism at Columbia University. After working three years at the *Sydney Morning Herald,* she was hired by the Cleveland bureau of the *Wall Street Journal,* who later sent her as a foreign correspondent, first to cover Australasia, then the Middle East (which led to her book *Nine Parts of Desire: The Hidden World of Islamic Women* [1995]), and finally Bosnia, Somalia, and Nigeria; she wrote of these days in her memoir, *Foreign Correspondence* (1998).

After an arrest in Nigeria, Brooks began to think about changing her career and finding ways to balance it with a family. She left the *Wall Street Journal* and soon after wrote her first work of historical fiction, *Year of Wonders* (2001), a novel set in the seventeenth century, in which the plague is transported out of London to a small country village that resolves to isolate itself to prevent further infection. This was followed by *March* (2005)—which won the 2006 Pulitzer Prize for Fiction—and most recently *People of the Book* (2008), a reconstructed tale of the Sarajevo Haggadah, one of the earliest illuminated Jewish manuscripts.

Though her novels are at times described as anachronistic, with contemporary sensibilities overlaid upon historical events, they are also richly researched and textured works, with remarkably strong narration and a powerful imaginative interplay that evokes the historical period in complex and subtle ways.

Considering the Novel

One of the items that attracts March's eye when he first enters the elegant reception hall on the plantation of Mr. Augustus Clement is *Bound Prometheus,* a sculpture that suggests something of Mr. Clement's wealthy, learned, ordered lifestyle. It refers, of course, to the punishment the gods meted out to the titan who dared to bring fire to humanity against the divine will. Twenty years later, March returns to that same hall and sees the sculpture again, but now the plantation house has been commandeered by the Union army as a hospital. When March enters, he sees a wounded soldier lying beneath the sculpture, his face portraying the same contortions that mark those of the agonized Prometheus. The sculpture strikes him again, perhaps because now its meaning is clearer: Prometheus was a being of high ideals and high hopes for bringing enlightenment—literally—to those in need. But he came up against a world not particularly interested in enlightenment, in which raw power and greed and anger and hatred and lust for possession overpower his ideals and leave him bound and tortured.

The sculpture is, in fact, an emblem of March's own life, for this is a novel that asks this question: Can a man of good intention, with high ideals, with a strong belief in the goodness of humanity and its growth toward maturity and refinement, with a central affirmation of human integrity—can such a man exist in a world of woe? Or, at best, can such a man stave off complete disillusionment, given the practical realities of the world around him? What does the man who is "interested in laying up the riches of the mind" (18) do when those riches are suddenly tarnished? What happens when a man is "dipped in the river of fire" (242)? What do you do with the tortured, agonized soldier beneath the elegant, classical statue?

March is at first strongly attracted to Augustus Clement, fascinated by his manner, by the well-run nature of his plantation, by his library, by the quality of his wide-ranging mind. He is, in fact, so astonished by Clement's capacities that he is led by Clement to believe that slavery itself is a necessary and good institution, a duty imposed on a more refined and cultured race to bring along an inferior race to a greater moral sensitivity; Clement's slaves, March concludes, are "fortunate" (27). Later, when he observes Grace being whipped for encouraging him to teach a slave child to read, he is disabused and comes to a different position. It takes a great deal to shock him to this new sensibility, so struck is he by Mr. Clement's high-mindedness, which seems, to him, to match his own. But when March dares to bring the fire of enlightenment to another, he sees the naked evil of the system firsthand. Lest the reader miss the huge shift in March's sensibility, Brooks uses names almost allegorically to show us how strongly March must be confronted: March observes Grace being whipped as fellow slaves Prudence and Justice—two of the cardinal virtues that Mr. Clement would have so prized—are forced, helplessly, to watch.

When we first meet March, he is idealistic and high-minded, yearning to be the teacher that leads others to his own nobility of mind. He believes his mission is attainable, but the reader and those around him—particularly the slaves—see him as naïve. When he begins teaching Prudence to read, he has been in Virginia for a full year, but he still seems unaware of the law against teaching a slave to read. He perceives Mr. Clement to be a kind and ordered governor of his estate and admires "the relations of affection and trust I had observed between master and servant" (24), but he fails to understand the undercurrents that suggest that there is another side to his governance. Despite multiple clues, March does not guess that Grace is Mr. Clement's daughter or that she has been violated by her brother. He fails to see the irony of the names of Annie's children, Prudence and Justice. Despite all of his vast reading, as Grace notes (31), he seems utterly impractical, utterly unable to negotiate his idealism in the avenues of the real world.

March is the Bound Prometheus, unable to understand or predict the failure of the ideal within the real world. He is unable to do anything with this dichotomy between the real and the ideal. Grace's brutal whipping forces him to see in Clement the failure of the idealized world he so admires to act righteously and well in the real world, but he can do nothing with this insight. When he leaves the estate, he attends a church meeting and points out the hypocrisy of sending funds to Africa for missionary needs while selling slaves in the marketplace next door—but he fails to go to the marketplace to free a single slave. When he crosses the river after the battle that opens the novel, he tries to save a wounded man—but by fending off the soldier's panic in the river, he loses him: "I wonder where he lies. Wedged under a rock, with a thousand small mouths already sucking on his spongy flesh. Or floating still, on and down, on and down, to wider, calmer reaches of the river" (8). When March returns to the Clement estate after twenty years, his duty is "to bring comfort where I could" (49), but he is unable to help a single wounded soldier in any real way, much as the doctor fails to save any soldier on whom he works. In short, his idealism is utterly ineffective. But March seems unaware of this ineffectiveness. While he rejects the stern Calvinism of the army chaplain, he fails to feel the harsh justice of the chaplain's own condemnation of March's vague theology as a "love poem" (8). The reader wonders if March isn't indeed the "loping nimshi" (31) his father named him.

The opening of the novel expresses March's ambivalence about his ability to even convey truth. He writes a cheerful, hopeful letter to his wife and daughters, in which he seems to speak out of his lofty high-minded world. "Do you recall the marbled end-papers in the Spenser that I used to read to you on crisp fall evenings just such as this? If so, then you, my dearest one, can see the sky as I saw it here tonight, for the colors swirled across the heavens in just such a happy profusion" (3). But in reality, the colors he is imagining are the colors of blood and the silt eddies of the river in which so many have just perished. He cannot express this to his daughters; perhaps, he believes, his silence will protect them. But in fact, it seems that his refusal to write the truth is a way to protect himself from the destruction of his own ideals. He muses that there is a reason that men have put their gods into the heavens above them: "For as soon as a man lets his eye drop from the heavens to the horizon, he risks setting it on some scene of desolation" (4). It is on the horizon that the Bound Prometheus dwells now. March does not want to look at the world as it truly is. He will write of Spenser's marbled pages instead.

Thus his sense that when he moves outside of his lofty world, he has moved into forbidden territory; usually, in his experience, this involves his encounters with Grace. When he first kisses her, his response sounds like something out of a sentimental novel: "The taste of her mouth was like cool spring water. The sweetness of it made me dizzy, and I wondered if I would be able to keep my feet" (34). He struggles between his lofty restraint and his passion, and he feels that he has failed when he yields to his passion. Twenty years later, he sees Grace again and tries to believe that his passion for her is a "moral act": "I wanted to give the lie to every claim of difference save the God-ordained one of Genesis: man and woman created he them" (56). But because he does try to be honest—at least to the reader—he also admits this: "I wanted her. The thought of her—arched, shuddering, abandoned—thrilled me to the core" (56). It is not clear whether the thrill is that of seeing her now, or that of recalling her whipping. He is not so free from this world of woe as he thinks; he, too, is bound.

Passion also dominates his responses to Marmee Day, who will become his wife. At first his responses seem very different from those he has given to Grace. Though her eyes astound him, he remarks that she is not beautiful, or even pretty—but "noble" (60). He is attracted, too, by her conversation, which she holds "with an open manner and a lack of affectation that I found remarkable and refreshing" (62). He also notes her sense of self-awareness: "I am one of those who knows how I wish the world were; I lack the discipline to make it so" (64), she notes. Which is, of course, exactly true of March, though he lacks the self-awareness to articulate it. But later, by the shores of Walden Pond, under the moon, with the flute of Henry Thoreau playing in the distance, his interest in her is quite different: "At the mere glimpse of her, my mental reservations were swept aside by my bodily longing. I called to her" (86). The scene is not particularly different from the earlier encounter with Grace, and suggests again the precariousness—or impossibility, or foolishness—of believing that one lives only on the ideal plain.

This opening section of the novel sets the trajectory of March's education in the real world, as he is forced to bring closer and closer together the world of his ideals and the world that he finds in his life directly around him. And it is a terrible forcing.

When twenty years have passed and he becomes a chaplain in the Union army, he still has not acknowledged in any real way the disjuncture between the ideal and the real; he has, in fact, become more certain of the ideal: "I find it suits me, this job of chaplain," he writes back to his wife, Marmee. "I am, indeed, a 'chapel man,' who carries within himself all that's needed for worship. At last, it is possible to have a part in faith without carved pulpit or Gothic arch, without lace altar cloth and without robes, save my suit of unornamented black" (58). The words are enormously self-satisfied, confident, and sure.

In fact, he is utterly wrong. The ideals that his self-satisfaction lead him to express as a chaplain seem superficial and naïve to those around him. After stopping an act of looting by Union soldiers, he brings the corporal in charge to the commanding officer, eager to have him rebuked. Instead, the rebuke is turned against him: "You can't seem to get on with anyone. You've irritated the other officers. . . . Even Tyndale can't abide you—and he's as much of an abolitionist as you are" (70). March tries to protest, but he is cut off and forced to face the strong gulf between his ideals and reality: "Be frank with yourself for once," asks the colonel. "Why, there're about as many genuine abolitionists in Lincoln's army as there are in Jeff Davis's. When the boys in this unit listen to you preach emancipation, all they hear is that a pack of ragged baboons is going to be heading north to take their jobs away" (70). But March will not be frank with himself; he never has been frank with himself. He refuses to believe that his ideals are not held elsewhere. It takes the colonel's threat of revealing his liaison with Grace to move March to accept another assignment—this one with the freed slaves who are trying an experiment in farming for pay and profit.

March arrives at this experiment with his ideals intact; his first act is to insist that young Jimse, only recently freed, ride on a mule as he walks beside him—again, his ideals overreaching the world around him. But here, in this place, he is finally brought irrevocably face to face with the failure of his ideals—though it is still very difficult for him to be frank about himself and about his world. He arrives with the words of the hymn on his lips—"his truth is marching on"—even as he recognizes that the "truth" he writes back home to his family is hardly truth at all. "Tomorrow should see me at last arrived at my assigned destination: a thousand liberated acres where the Negros now under our protection are learning the sweet savor of toil performed for the reward of wages. My heart is light tonight, as I think about my part in this first great experiment of equality" (89), he writes home. Yet immediately upon arriving, he makes judgments based upon these ideals, accusing the manager, Ethan Canning, of cruelty and neglect. Canning's response, "You know exactly nothing" (104), is accurate. March makes judgments knowing nothing about the real situation in which Canning finds himself. March does not realize the sacrifices that Canning has made, the conditions under which he works, the things he has had to learn as a manager that he had never planned on, the fact that some slaves still serve the Rebels, and the fact that Canning drives no one on the farm harder than he drives himself. He does not even realize that Canning comes with a dual vision: first, to make a good living and a profit, and second, to better the position of the freed slaves:

> I don't claim to be an evangel of abolition like you, Mr. March. I'm a businessman, simple as that. Yet we both have a role to play in the betterment of the Negro's condition. I came here with more than an ordinary interest in the free labor enterprise. I believe that the production of cotton and sugar by free labor must be both possible and profitable . . . for *them* as well as us. If we cannot prove our point, what future will these people have? (97)

He is, in short, well beyond March in marrying his ideals to the real world. But March is still unsure. So Canning advises, "Don't be a simpleton, March" (109), and his voice seems one in a long line. It is, in fact, echoed soon after, when March wonders why the Union general does not shut down a general store that supports the Rebel marauders: "Chaplain, you sure is an innocent man!" (138), the soldiers laugh. This innocence culminates in March's refusal to head to a safe place once the Union garrison is drawn down and there is no longer any protection for the farm. He is a noncombatant, he tells Jesse, who works on the farm with him. There are rules in war, and "the Confederate soldier is a hard and desperate fighter, but he is not a savage" (164).

Another set of ideals: There are rules in war. Men are not savages. But again, March is wrong, as he finds out in the most violent, horrific section of the novel. Rebel marauders do come, and there are no rules, and they are savages. They shoot Canning in both knees and cut off his ear. They burn the buildings down and destroy the crops. They behead one of the slaves and gather sixty more to sell. They bring the maimed Canning with them to ransom. When March and Jesse follow to attempt a rescue, their plan is utterly foiled by March's inability to use any sort of violence. Canning is shot in the face, some of the sixty slaves killed, Jesse captured, and he himself left to die. His miraculous rescue plunges him into a deep fever, so deep that even the narrative point of view shifts, and the voice becomes that of Marmee—who will discover that beneath the high ideals of her husband lies, possibly, an adulterous affair.

Now there is no place for March to hide, except in unconsciousness. The judgments of the colonel, of the soldiers, of Canning, of Annie, of Grace, of Augustus Clement—all of these come upon him. His innocence and idealism are not only impractical in the real world, they are disastrous. Everything that he has turned his hand to has failed—horribly. The world is not the place he thought it was; love poems are not enough to turn the human heart. There is cruelty and wickedness and horror, and he is unable to eradicate these. His judgments have all been wrong, and those he has tried to help are dead or enslaved. Even Jimse, the sweet boy whose curls he keeps, is dead. And he realizes, too, that his ideals have placed his own wife and daughters in a position of poverty and servitude.

The trajectory toward March's realization that the ideal and the real world must be in conflict is not a straight one. There are times when he recognizes that reality will put the lie to the high-minded vision. Before he heads to the contraband experiment that will go so horribly wrong, he notes how frequently the ideal is not able to play out: "How often it is that an idea that seems bright bossed and gleaming in its clarity when examined in a church, or argued over with a friend in a frosty garden, becomes clouded and murk-stained when dragged out into the field of actual endeavor" (65). But he is unable to act upon this realization any more than he can tell the truth in his letters to his wife: "And every day, as I turn to what should be the happy obligation of opening my mind to my wife, I grope in vain for words with which to convey to her even a part of what I have witnesses, what I have felt" (65). Language, he finds, is not to convey truth, but in fact to hide and screen truth—until such time that that which is hidden is so open, so undeniable, so unable to be screened, that it must be told and consequences faced—even consequences that destroy utterly all ideals.

In this tumbled world, he lies in a hospital bed and must see himself in an entirely new light. His idealism, he recognizes, is falsehood. So, what to do now? The ideal cannot exist within the real, outside of personal blindness. And here, the novel does not posit any easy answer to the question of what to do with this new realization. When Marmee comes to the hospital, she suggests that one way to live is to recognize limitations; he is not responsible for the deaths around him; it is the cause of the war. "You are not God," she tells him. "You do not determine the outcome. The outcome is not the point" (258). But March finds this rationalization wholly inadequate. When he asks what the point might be, she gives a sentimental and clichéd response: "The point is the effort" (258). She acknowledges frustration when the ideal comes up against the real: "To believe, to act, and to have events confound you—I grant you, that is hard to bear" (258). She, too, is struggling with the same loss of the ideal, as she has learned that much of her marriage has been, she thinks, false. But March cannot accept the clichéd response or the easy absolution of guilt. The ghosts hover around him, and he feels it is only just to allow them their play. He resolves that he cannot return home until he has atoned for his failures.

But other answers to the problem of the ideal come as well. One comes in the poem of the dead solider Cephas White, who writes just before his death, "I am no longer eager, bold & strong. / All that is past; / I am ready not to do / At last, at last" (265). The words strike March as wise; perhaps he, too, must be "ready not to do"—that is, not to foist his own idealism upon others, but to live in the world he finds. And this realization seems confirmed by Grace, who is now his nurse, as she urges him to return home to his family who need him, and to live in the world he finds, not the world he has imagined and hoped for: "I simply ask you to see that there is only one thing to do when we fall, and that is to get up, and go on with the life that is set in front of us, and try to do the good of which our hands are capable for the people who come in our way" (268). The freed slaves, she says, do not need him: "There are Negro preachers aplenty who know the true language of our souls. A free people must learn to manage its own destiny" (268)—immediately depriving him even of the self-satisfied sense that the role of the chaplain suits him well. "Be a father to your daughters. That, at least, you can do" (269). And he knows that this much is so. He heads home, where he feels that he is dissimulating as his daughters gather around him, until Beth, weakened by fever, rushes toward him, and "instinct opened my arms and I caught her—frail wisp that even I, depleted, could hold without effort" (271).

There are many ways in which the character of March is unlikable. He is arrogant and too sure of his idealism. He seems, at times, proud in his humility. He carries a terrible flaw in his inability to close the gap between the real and the ideal, and seems to be unwilling to disabuse himself of his own innocence. He is the idealist who lacks wisdom.

But, even as we recognize that the idealist may not be able to live in the real world, we long for the ideals, and we long for them to be embodied—even in these clay pots that are our selves. We want there to be more in the world, and there is a strong sense in the novel that March, though he fails, fails while trying to point to something that is real and substantive and noble.

One of the paradoxes of the world is that the ideal *is* embodied in the real—and in very concrete ways. And this is what stories can point to: to see the ideal in the flawed real. Shouldn't there be more in the world beyond the merely real? stories ask. Shouldn't there be ideals we reach for, knowing we can never reach them? And even if characters like March fail, aren't we all the better for the dreamers, despite the costs? Or should Prometheus have never brought fire down to us at all?

Discussion Questions about the Novel

1. *March* is a mixture of sources, including *Little Women* and the letters and diaries of Bronson Alcott, Louisa May Alcott's father. In what ways might a reading of *March* be enriched by a knowledge of these sources? Or, is a knowledge of these sources not merely enriching but a necessity? If so, does such a dependency suggest any failure on the part of the novel's craft?

2. Some have suggested that the character of March is anemic, weak, and really unable to carry a first-person narrative. Do you agree? Would this have been a stronger novel if it had been told by an outside narrator? How might that have changed our understandings of March, Grace, and Marmee?

3. One of the great American myths is that of the possibility of self-improvement. It is this myth to which March ascribes in *Little Women*, as he enjoins his daughters to always be about the task of improving the self. Does *March* seem to be a novel about self-improvement in any sense? Perhaps one way to approach this question is to examine March's realization—a realization that is slow in coming—that his idealism does not seem to work in the real world. He resolves, then, to "set my feet on the path of atonement, and find some niche in which a diminished man could be of modest use" (262–63). Does the novel suggest that this is an appropriate path for March? Is atonement a form of self-improvement?

4. The voice of March dominates the narrative, but during his convalescence, while he is as a character insensible, the voice of Marmee takes over the story. She finds out truths about her husband that she had not known, and comes to recognize, too, that words may be screens. Is this sudden shift in narrative point of view—a shift that extends for a few chapters, and is then dropped—a flaw in the novel's construction? Or does it help us understand March and Marmee better?

5. The word *March*, of course, refers to the protagonist's last name. But *march* is also a noun and a verb. "The Battle Hymn of the Republic," from which the protagonist quotes, contains the well-known line, "His truth is marching on." And such marching seems appropriate to March's notion of the progression of the ideal. There is also the sense that the title can be a call to action, as if the reader, too, should be about the business of marching. But to where, and to what purpose? How might a consideration of the title in such ways

be productive in terms of your understanding of what March comes to learn through his own marching?

6. Is it fair to say that March's idealism colors the narrative? For example, we might argue that Grace is too idealistic a character. But is this true only because we see her through the eyes of March—and later, Marmee? Certainly March is himself accused of idealizing characters about whom he knows nothing. Does this tendency steer him toward becoming an unreliable narrator?

Other Books to Consider

—John Banville, *The Sea*. New York: Knopf, 2005.

> When Max Morden realizes that his life is being dominated by overwhelming disturbances, he decides to travel back to the seaside of his childhood, where one summer a half-century earlier, he had encountered the Grace family—with shattering consequences. The narrator moves between the story of that summer and the more recent slow death of his wife, but nothing is predictable, and much is illusory as the past and present intersect. Like March, Morden must face the past with guilt and sadness and regret, and find a way to try to live in the very real present.

—Denise Giardina, *Storming Heaven*. New York: Ballantine Books, 1987.

> In Annadel, West Virginia, the coal company has stolen everything once owned by a small, close, family-oriented town. The story is told from four points of view, all focused on the ways in which people struggle to maintain ideals in the face of huge corporate greed—a greed supported by the power structures of the United States government.

—Sena Jeter Naslund, *Ahab's Wife: Or, The Star-gazer*. New York: William Morrow, 1999.

> An adventure, a romance of epic proportions, this novel follows the career of Una Spenser, who escapes a restrictive religious home to move to the east coast of Massachusetts, where she will meet, in addition to historical figures such as Maria Mitchell and Margaret Fuller, Melville's Ahab. Their mutual passion and fierce desire to strike through the veil unites them in a novel whose construction vividly recalls *March*.

—Edith Wharton, *Ethan Frome*. New York: Scribner's, 1911.

> When Ethan is a young man, he dreams of becoming an engineer and traveling the world. But when sickness comes to his family and he marries out of obligation rather than for love, it seems as if his earlier ideals have all given way to the gray reality of his life. Then, unexpectedly, Mattie Silver, his wife's cousin, comes to live with them—and the earlier ideals are rekindled, along with thoughts of love and passion.

INTUITION Allegra Goodman
(2006)

In the mid-eighties, before giant pharmaceuticals sup-
planted the government as the primary funding source for
medical research, Cliff Bannaker, a young postdoctoral
microbiologist, appears to have made a dazzling discovery
in cancer research. A new version of his previously unprom-
ising R-7 virus, with which he has worked for countless
months, suddenly appears to be shrinking tumors into
oblivion. A remarkable percentage of sick mice become
healthy as their tumors disappear. His blockbuster discovery quickly elevates Cliff, who had been teetering on the
brink of dismissal, to favorite son status in the lab. Success
catapults him into an arena of adulation and favor. God or
luck has transformed a hopeless, dying research project into
a promising beacon of hope for everyone.

Marion Mendelssohn and Sandy Glass, the lab's codirectors, marshal every available resource, including his fellow
postdocs, to pursue the promises signaled by Cliff's initial
results. One of them, Xiang Feng, nearly supplants Cliff's
notoriety when *People* magazine features an article on the
lab and its promising new research. Feng seems happy as
long as the spotlight shines broadly enough to include him.
Other postdocs, most notably Cliff's girlfriend, Robin,
are less enthusiastic about tailoring their efforts to serve
Cliff's hot new project. Only weeks before the big discovery, Marion and Sandy had been ready to shift Cliff from
his own stillborn project to assist Robin with hers. Now as
Cliff's stock rises and she has been harnessed to his task,

Robin's resentment begins to smolder. Why should she lay aside her project, her future, to serve the interests of a slightly junior colleague?

As the novel moves along, personal interests continue to seep into the pursuit of pure science as the lab attempts to extend and confirm the results of Cliff's discovery. A pressing need for fresh funding fires Sandy Glass's natural inclination to showmanship, prompting him to publish results early, perhaps even prematurely, in order to stoke up as much enthusiasm for future funding as possible. Marion Mendelssohn's more cautious disposition places her in an increasingly tense relationship with Sandy. She feels that they should wait longer for confirmation of the results before going public, but how long will that be?

Robin increasingly resents Cliff as he steals time from their relationship to pour into his research. Her resentment grows as Cliff basks in the limelight and as appreciation for her own efforts founder. Further animosity develops as she suspects that in his enthusiasm to advance the work, Cliff has been tempted to cut corners and bend Marion's meticulously cautious rules of procedure. The novel plays itself out within this growing web of personal tension and drive for scientific discovery, leaving the reader to wonder how the initial discovery will pan out and whether relationships under such strain will continue to hold together.

On the Author

Allegra Goodman (b. 1967) grew up in an Orthodox Jewish family in Honolulu, Hawaii, where she wrote and illustrated her first novel at age seven. There she attended and graduated from Punahou School (1985), an institution that also includes President Barack Obama (1979) among its prominent graduates. After high school, she pursued studies at Harvard University, where she received an AB degree, and later earned a PhD in English Literature from Stanford University.

Goodman comes by her interest in science and scientists honestly. Her mother, Madeline Goodman, taught population genetics at the University of Hawaii and later moved to Vanderbilt. Certain features of *Intuition* track the experiences of her sister, Paula Fraenkel, a researcher and oncologist, and those of her husband, David Karger, a computer scientist. She has a feel for the pressures under which scientists work, their persistent need for funding, their instability within a lab's shifting pecking order, and their abiding fear that someone else may make and publish their discovery before they do.

Goodman now lives in Cambridge, Massachusetts. In addition to a book of short stories, *The Family Markowitz* (1996), Goodman has published five other novels, including her first novel, the critically acclaimed *Kaaterskill Falls* (1998).

Considering the Novel

In *Intuition,* Goodman puts notions of truth, presumption, intuition, and human nature under the microscope in the controlled setting of a cancer research laboratory. In theory and in the popular imagination, science is all about truth, and in this laboratory, scientists seek the truth—scientific truth—almost as if it were a religion. The best scientists, like Marion Mendelssohn, one of the lab's codirectors, have "a purity about them, a desire for truth as an end in itself" (215). But truth and its purity come under assault in this microcosm of the scientific world. God may have been pushed off stage, but what in a nonscientific world might be called sin has certainly made an intrusive entrance.

The novel opens with Cliff Bannaker under pressure for continuing to explore possibilities in a research project that his supervisors, Marion Mendelssohn and Sandy Glass, have judged untenable. They have ordered him to cease, but he has delayed foreclosure on his beloved project. Now Mendelssohn and Glass have called him in for a meeting to tell him to shut his project down, and Cliff begins to wonder if his persistence has prompted him to violate the canons of scientific truth: "A scientist was, by definition, impassive. He cut his losses and moved on to something else; he was exhausted, perhaps, but never defiant with exhaustion. A scientist did not allow emotion to govern his experiments" (6–7).

Has something, perhaps an emotional attachment to this project into which he had poured thousands of hours, led Cliff away from a proper pursuit of the truth? Cliff's self doubt raises questions about how anyone within the scientific world knows if he or she is pursuing real truth or some fanciful, whimsical chimera. From where do these impulses toward truth or away from it come? How can one account for the intuition that tempts the scientist to pursue alleys that may be blind?

The novel suggests intuition and creativity as important features that guide the scientist. Creativity is that quality of the human person that somehow allows him or her to see and make connections between things not obviously connected. Marion's husband, Jacob, is one of those scientists who discovers early in his career that, though brilliant in many ways, he is bereft of creativity:

> As he solved a myriad minor problems in cell biology, and studied the scientific literature—as he watched Applebaum direct his lab, choosing investigative paths, deciding where to invest his time and experimental energy—Jacob identified in himself a fatal inability to

generate new problems. . . . In short Jacob realized that he was not creative. . . . He lacked the second sight to shape new paradigms and shake up the world with revolutionary propositions. (32–33)

Goodman associates this creativity with intuition, which can be defined as the direct knowing or learning of something without the conscious use of reason. Intuition is the sort of insight that encourages artists and scientists to see connections. Intuition is that inner "something" that prompts and pushes, that gives knowledge through a meta-process outside rational scientific inquiry. But identifying creativity or intuition as a mysteriously given source of guidance raises deeper questions. If creativity or intuition delivers truth—or guidance toward truth—to people who have a gift for receiving it, what is the source of this gift?

People of faith would, no doubt, point to God. God embeds the truth in the created world and then gives people the ability to discern it. Intuition and creativity are God-given powers. But God and religion do not fare especially well in this novel, not much better than they often do in the scientific world more generally. Neither of the directors of the lab in *Intuition* have a deep and lively religious faith. Sandy Glass remembers the trappings of the Jewish faith of his childhood "with a certain nostalgia" (15). His wife, Ann, embraces religious faith in much the same tepid way. She was raised Episcopalian, but "she lit the menorah every year because she felt it was important for the children" (15). In the Glass household, religion is a quaint vestige of the past that apparently embodies a level of truth, if you can call it that, suitable only for children.

Religious faith in Marion Mendelssohn's life is not any more robust than in the Glass household. The Mendelssohns also practice their religious faith mostly as an artifact of the past. Marion celebrates Passover not to remember the great acts of God in history but "in memory of her parents" (144). Marion's husband, Jacob, reads the Haggadah, the Passover story, from a rendering by his late father, a liberal rabbi. Its incipient universalism and annoying attempts to parallel Milton's *Paradise Lost* aggravate Jacob, but he admires his father, "who understood intuitively that the old science [of religion] must give way to new" (148). After the Haggadah reading, one of the Passover guests makes the point that "the ten plagues could be read as metaphors for environmental catastrophe":

> The water turns to blood, right? The country is overrun with frogs. We've got sickness in the cattle. Boils. It's the whole ecosystem out of whack. And yet the pharaoh ignores each new problem that comes up. The whole order of nature is upended, and the government looks the other way. That's very powerful to me. (149)

Here the best that religion can do is to articulate scientific truth in an imprecise, metaphorical way.

Intuition certainly highlights features of scientific religion. The novel suggests that science as it functions in the lives of many scientists has certain religious qualities. People in *Intuition*'s scientific community hold to the fundamental worth and reliability of science with almost religious conviction. Robin's neighbors, a couple of computer scientists, are typical: "Larry and Wendy were both atheists, of course, but they kept the scientific faith, hallowing intellectual honesty, and technology, and the pursuit of progress" (203).

Like religious faith, the religious features of science exhibit communal aspects and find expression in families. Marion finds her own faith in science supported and buttressed by the faith of her codirector, Sandy Glass: "Agnostic that she was, she'd leaned on him for his scientific faith. She had never considered how pure that faith had been, flaming so strong with such scant data to support him" (354). Though members of Sandy's family were not scientists, his scientific faith informed their own. In the family, this faith finds both expression and support. In the case of Sandy's children,

> their identities were all tied up to his, wrapped up in his cause and his career. His brilliance was the centerpiece of their family. His impossible hours, his weekends on call, his absences had structured their lives. His work as a healer, his research, his arrogant benevolence of all comprised the central myth of their childhood, and they half dreaded the demolition of that myth, the smashing of their household god. What would become of the family then? What new religion would guide them? (309–10)

Oddly, what, in theory, should have persisted as belief in the pure ideals of science has become inextricably intertwined with faith in a person, and every person in the novel fails to measure up to the purity of those scientific ideals.

In religion, people call this failure to measure up "sin," but in the novel scientists tend to have a rather undeveloped or underdeveloped sense of sin. When Kate, Sandy's youngest daughter, mentions sin in a discussion with him about her interest in the poet John Donne, Sandy laughs aloud. For Sandy, so steeped in the world of science, "the very word was archaic, to his mind. Sin was like some dread medieval contagion long ago contained, some previously invisible microbe carried by rats or fleas" (89). But something like the contagion that Sandy thought had been long ago contained has appeared and infected the laboratory community that he leads. The devolution of the Mendelssohn-Glass lab community and the relationships within it drives the plot of this novel. Far more than questions about what causes Cliff's apparently successful cancer treatment to fail, the novel painstakingly explores the contagion of human weakness that can assault pure science and leave a scientific community broken, its faith shaken.

At the beginning of the novel, the contagion is detectable but apparently limited and relatively harmless. Cliff's selfish inability to follow the directives of his lab supervisors looks like an isolated, containable instance of the disease. Yes, there will be consequences. As Cliff's late thesis advisor put it: "What do you expect? You don't listen to the lab director, you get busted" (10). This is hardly contagion spinning out of control. In this limited instance, selfish impulse has transformed pure, scientific intuition into presumption. If he were to have been guided by pure intuition, he would have sized up the futility of his own research and, with his mentors' guidance, known enough to quit. But the selfishness that infects Cliff pushes him to presume that his research ought to continue. Still, at this early stage, his selfish choice looks harmless for everyone but Cliff. The contagion apparently will take a mostly unremarkable toll as Marion and Sandy confront Cliff and cull him from the scientific community so he will not, as Sandy Glass informs Cliff, "drag everyone else down with your personal flights of fancy" (7).

But when Cliff's research yields its apparently remarkable results, the contagion shows new life right along with his clinically dead research. No sooner has the import of his possible cancer cure seen the light of day than the virus of human selfishness begins to multiply and assert itself as well. This time it is not just Cliff, but both Cliff and Robin who show the initial symptoms of the disease. Cliff gets up early on the day he is to inoculate the next set of mice with his miracle virus. Robin already senses that Cliff's dedication to this promising scientific enterprise is beginning to come between them:

> "It's not even six." She sat up with the sheet covering her and pulled her knees up to her chin. "Why don't we have breakfast and go in together?"
>
> "No, you don't understand . . ."
>
> "Right, how could I," she shot back offended.
>
> "I'm sorry, I'm sorry," he murmured, even as he pulled on his clothes. "Please, Robin." But unspoken, the facts forced their way between them. He had results and she didn't. His experiments were like Christmas; every morning he had new questions to unwrap, but Robin had no new worlds to conquer.
>
> "I'll see you soon?" he asked her.
>
> "Just go," she said. (54–55)

Infected with selfishness, Robin is jealous of Cliff's success, and as a victim of the same disease, he is insensitive to her feelings. But this early in the story, the contagion seems only to have affected their domestic relationship, not their scientific work.

But that same day, the disease makes an appearance at the lab. By going in early to inject his mice with the next round of the virus, Cliff, out of selfish enthusiasm, fails to include Xiang Feng in the procedure. Cliff regrets this exclusion, but the damage has been done:

> Still, as he threw his used syringes into the plastic bio-hazard containers, Cliff felt a twinge of guilt to see Feng standing there empty-handed. Cliff could have waited two hours and allowed Feng to inject the mice with him. Being a team player, or a friend, for that matter—these

> were things Cliff valued. . . . The injections had gone
> well. Cliff should have been able to share that with Feng.
> It was just that Cliff held possible results so tantalizing
> and so precious that he couldn't, even for an instant,
> open his hand. (56)

The disease has yet to affect his scientific work adversely, but it is
no longer limited only to the domestic front.

Something of an older contagion also seems to have come out
of remission in the lab's directors. Marion is reluctant to tell
Sandy about the initial results of Cliff's apparent breakthrough.
She is cautious because she knows that "when it came to science,
Sandy's motives were not entirely pure. . . . Sandy's work was
not about giving of himself, but about building up himself, his
ego, and his persona" (36–37). His self-regard has slipped the
thin edge of the wedge between colleagues who, at this crucial
moment of an apparently earthshaking scientific discovery, need
each other's critical assessment strengths. But while Sandy may
have the more virulent strain of the disease, Marion is not unaf-
fected either. Sandy notices that Marion too "wanted more than
a private sense of accomplishment. She wanted glory" (79). As a
result, she may be less willing to restrain Sandy when glory and
grandeur for herself are also a possibility.

But we are still in the early stages of the outbreak. Selfishness
also works to taint the purity of their science, a pursuit that ideally
ought to be followed for its own sake, for its truth or beauty.
With the presence of the disease, less noble goals motivate and
overshadow scientific purity. Marion pursues scientific discovery
at least in part for selfish glory. Sandy has the same penchant
for glory with a hankering for money as well. "The world," he
observes, "is full of questions to be answered, diseases to investigate, not to mention—God forbid—money to be made" (63). The
stage is set for an even more acute outbreak of selfishness.

As selfishness grows, the disease pushes intuition into presumption and truth toward error. Robin begins to revise the history of her relationship with Cliff through the eyes of envy: "He'd usurped Robin's position, beating her out for money, space, time, attention. From the first day he'd had special treatment, and it infuriated her that he would not acknowledge that" (69). Resentment grows as Robin feels that Cliff has "crushed her with his success" (73). Under the pressure of his arrogance and her jealousy, their relationship falls apart. He insinuates that she is incompetent, and she suspects that he has cut corners. Maybe this is why she is unable to reproduce his results.

Science tainted by selfishness continues at a fever pace. In the grip of selfishness, Sandy presumes to publish Cliff's results prematurely. Sandy's longing for money and fame push him, and Marion's secret longing for the same prompts her to acquiesce. She objects to Sandy's allowing *People* magazine to popularize their discovery that has yet to be adequately confirmed, but something keeps her from really resisting when the reporters actually show up. The community that is supposed to work to insure accountability has begun to break down under the influence of the disease of human selfishness.

Further breakdown commences as jealousy prompts Robin to presume the worst about Cliff. He has either deliberately or inadvertently falsified his data: "Her intuition told her Cliff had cheated" (204). But the disease has prompted her to suppose that her presumption is true intuition. She searches the lab for documentation that will verify her presumptions, and ends up acquiring Cliff's unauthorized draft notes that she further assumes serve as evidence of his cheating. As her jealousy goads her on, she engineers an outside review of the work that she already has decided is bogus.

As self-interest intertwines itself with pure science, intuition gives way to presumption. When the outside review fails to verify her suspicions, self-regarding indignation prompts Robin to push the matter further. The disease rages on as Robin contacts a disgruntled former employee of the lab who entices her into taking her suspicions to ORIS, the investigative arm of the National Institute of Health. The contagion reaches epidemic proportions as ORIS launches its investigation, a U.S. senator joins in with a congressional investigation as an occasion for self-promotion, and day after day every sort of accusation and innuendo plays itself out in the press.

In the end, the disease of human selfishness destroys the lab and its scientific community. The once promising team of Mendelssohn and Glass splits apart. Sandy leaves pure science behind to direct the Stoughton Clinic, where, without Marion, he stands in danger of succumbing to the allure of its money and losing his soul in the pragmatism of administration. Marion resolves to start anew, but without Sandy's evangelical scientific zeal to inspire and carry her, the future looks less than promising. Cliff's work with the R-7 virus, which perhaps still holds some promise, receives a vote of no confidence from Marion, who decides to retract the article that reported the initial work in *Nature* (359). After the contagion of human selfishness and self-interest has run its course, every significant relationship among the scientists lies in ruins and their once promising project stands as a ruined tower of presumption with its workers scattered.

Scientists, at least the ones in this novel, assume that science discovers pure objective truth. Religion, as understood by the minds of *Intuition*'s scientific community, at best voices personal, metaphorical insights of which science speaks more clearly and precisely. For readers with spiritual sensitivities, these claims raise issues of the nature of spiritual truth. Certainly when spiritual truth is rooted in historical claims or human experience, these can be investigated in ways similar to those used to evaluate scientific truth. Issues of self-interest of the sort that come into play in *Intuition* also appear in religion and must be taken into account. In this sense, while the novel may prompt religion to ask about its standards of truth, it also challenges science to consider the source of its truth, whether anything like sin operates within it, and the religious quality of its quest.

Discussion Questions about the Novel

1. Goodman tells us that Sandy recognizes something that Marion could never admit: "She wanted more than a private sense of accomplishment. She wanted glory" (79). Longing for personal glory can lead a person to self-promotion or to denigrate and belittle the accomplishments of rivals. But is longing for glory always a bad thing? What might a pure, untainted longing for glory look like?

2. Does forgiveness or grace function within the scientific world of the novel? Goodman informs us that "Marion was constitutionally incapable of apology. Robin would not be forgiven for turning against the lab, for showing Marion such disrespect" (384). Yet how are we to understand Marion's calling on Robin as she looks to be acknowledged during the question-and-answer part of Marion's conference presentation at the very end of the book? Is this an act of grace?

3. The novel suggests that one of the things in which religion specializes needs to be taken into account more fully in science, namely the degree to which sin and evil impact the scientific quest. How might the scientific community more

openly deal with the effect of human frailty on the scientific project? On the other hand, does science have something to say to religion about standards of truth at a time when religious hucksters still entice us from our television screens and ask for our money?

4. The novel suggests that science pursues truth, although it also mentions beauty as a reason for pursuing it. For Marion, "experiments were beautiful" (138). What is the place of beauty in science and in religion, and how are the two related?

5. Contemporary culture often embraces the relativity of truth or, at least as Cliff claims, "truth depends on context" (279). Is context important both for religious truth and for scientific truth, or more for one than the other?

6. Marion's husband, Jacob, realizes at one point in the novel that "he had given Robin a dangerous gift; he had given her his own skepticism" (219). Skepticism protects a person from being duped, but it can also prevent legitimate belief. What is the place of skepticism in faith?

Other Books to Consider

—Andrea Barrett, *Ship Fever*. New York: W.W. Norton, 1996.

> In the title story of this collection, typhus rages as a young Quebec doctor copes with an epidemic and issues surrounding the care of its victims. In eight tales set in the middle of the nineteenth century, Barrett explores the ways in which human curiosity is nourished by both spiritual belief and scientific progress—and how the connections between these two might be one way to understand the workings of the human soul.

—Francis Collins, *The Language of God: A Scientist Presents Evidence for Belief*. New York: Simon and Schuster, 2006.

The director of the human genome project explores the relationship between faith and science, particularly in the area of genetics.

—Madeline L'Engle, *A Wrinkle in Time*. New York: Farrar, Strauss, and Cudahy, 1962.

Meg, her scientist parents, and genius little brother live in the interfaces between science and spirituality. They must rely on their abilities to negotiate these interfaces as they try to rescue their father from a world dominated by a brutal, unloving intellect.

—C.S. Lewis, *That Hideous Strength: A Modern Fairy-Tale for Grown-Ups*. London: The Bodley Head, 1945.

In the final book of his Space Trilogy, Lewis explores the Promethean possibilities of science as Ransom battles an agency that believes persons are unimportant—only scientific advance matters.

FIELDWORK Mischa Berlinski
(2007)

Synopsis

Twenty-eight-year-old Mischa Berlinski (the name of the narrator as well as the name of the author) is an American living in Thailand who cobbles together a living writing articles for magazines and newspapers. When he finds himself in Bangkok chasing down quotes for a story, he looks up an old friend, Josh O'Connor, who promptly embroils him in another story, a murder mystery of sorts: An American anthropologist, Martiya van der Leun, has been confined to a Thai prison for the murder of a young American missionary, David Walker. O'Connor has been to visit her, and she, in turn, has entrusted two ethnographic essays to him, which she asks him to forward to the appropriate academic journals. Intrigued, O'Connor calls the prison for more information, only to be informed that van der Leun has committed suicide. "Maybe you can write it up for the *Times*," he tells Berlinksi, who accepts the challenge to learn more about the murder, Martiya's life, and her suicide.

As the novel unfolds, Berlinski not only discovers more information about Martiya, but also becomes involved in the multigenerational saga of the Walker clan, who have been missionaries in Asia for over sixty years. He learns that the conflict between the anthropologist and missionaries began long before the murder and turns on their differing perceptions of the Dyalo tribe, whose own story becomes central to the novel. Berlinski, who tries to maintain an objective journalist stance, finds himself increasingly intrigued by the religious and personal passions that animate anthropologists, missionaries, and tribal people alike, and his account of their intertwined stories—the novel *Fieldwork*—attempts to do justice to this multilayered narrative.

Mischa Berlinski (b. 1973) was born and raised in New York City, studied at the University of California in Berkeley and Columbia University, and has worked in Thailand as a journalist. During a vacation in India, he met two American brothers, sons of missionaries, who at the time were making their living by selling hashish. Despite their current lifestyle, Berlinski sensed that their itinerant drug dealing would only be "a parenthesis in a pair of otherwise solid Christian lives," and he later merged them into the character of David Walker in *Fieldwork*.

While living in Thailand, he met dozens of missionaries and discovered, to his amazement, that they were quite ordinary and sane people. As he said in an interview for the Festival of Faith and Writing at Calvin College, "They had rich, intense family lives and modest habits and enjoyed a good gossip. I liked them. . . . And they had an understanding of Thailand and of the Lisu that was deep and rich and profound." Although at first he wanted to write a history of the conversion of the Lisu people, an ethnic minority in southeast Asia, to Christianity, no publisher accepted his proposal, and he converted his research into a novel. *Fieldwork*, his first book, was nominated for the National Book Award in 2007.

Considering the Novel

Fieldwork is a novel that is packed with stories—lots and lots of stories about lots and lots of people. In the first thirty pages we are introduced to Josh O'Connor, an expatriate who "has done just about every sort of odd job a foreigner in Thailand can do" (3); to the narrator, Mischa Berlinski, whose girlfriend, Rachel, teaches first graders at the Water Lily International School while he freelances as a journalist; to Martiya van der Leun, an American anthropologist who has been sentenced to serve fifty years at the Chiang Mai Central Prison for murder; and to Martiya's elderly aunt in Holland, whose husband has left his niece a small inheritance. We also meet an assortment of supporting characters: Wim DeKlerk, an attaché at the Dutch embassy; Uncle Otto, the prime minister's nephew; Dirk, the "practical, kindly" Dutch engineer whose lectures on technology are "*unbearably* irritating" (28); the Thai street food vendors; Baiyom, Mischa's Yoda-like neighbor who sits on the floor with her legs straight out and slashes bamboo cane to hold up his badminton net; the discontented teachers at Rachel's school, and so on. Some of these characters become central to the plot (Mischa, Martiya, and Rachel), others reappear on occasion (Josh, Baiyom, and the teachers), and yet others simply disappear (Dirk and the prime minister's nephew). One of the most important sets of characters, David Walker and his clan, does not appear in this opening list at all. But if you have ever started a research project, perhaps looking up your genealogy or trolling through the Internet for information on a country you hope to visit, you will know how difficult it is to determine at the outset of an investigation—fieldwork, as it is called in anthropology—exactly who or what will be important. Anthropologists, journalists, travelers, and researchers of all stripes begin simply by describing everything they see, and

Fieldwork uses this wide-angle lens to pull us, the readers, along with Mischa as he is sucked into the vortex of Martiya's story.

Mischa soon discovers that Martiya's life can be divided into three parts: her childhood, her years as a budding anthropologist, and her later life among the Dyalo tribespeople in northern Thailand. The daughter of a Dutch linguist father and an unhappy Malaysian mother, Martiya was born in Indonesia and grew up in a Tobaku village on the island of Sulawesi, an only child beloved of her parents and the local villagers. Although she leaves the island for America at age seven, after the accidental— or suicidal—death of her mother, Sulawesi remains home, the core of her identity, for the rest of her life. "If asked to state her ethnicity . . ." Mischa discovers, "she would always respond that she was *topo'uma*—a user of the Uma language, the same response any villager who lived near the mighty Lariang River in southern Kulawi District would have given" (30).

Being *topo'uma* makes Martiya an exotic outsider at Berkeley, where her father takes up a position as professor of linguists, as does her animosity against the communists who oppressed ethnic minority tribal people throughout Southeast Asia. "She voted for Nixon," a former boyfriend exclaims in disbelief. "Twice" (36). It is no surprise, then, that she drifts toward a major in anthropology, the department "for a lot of folks who didn't feel at home anywhere else" (37) and toward one of its star professors, Joseph Atkinson, who had done his own fieldwork among the Doyo in French West Africa. Atkinson had returned to the States and the professoriate after five years, sporting a "handsome silver eel-shaped wound" (46) across his neck, the result of his participation in intratribal warfare. The publicity photographs on the backs of his books, all of them descriptions and redescriptions of his life among the Doyo, were posed to show the scar with greatest dramatic effect.

The ultimate test for an anthropologist, Martiya knows, is to do such original ethnographic fieldwork, to live in a completely different culture (preferably tribal and preliterate), to observe and record everyday life, and to write a thorough, nonjudgmental description—an ethnography—of this group of people. An anthropologist is thus faced with often contradictory and sometimes incompatible goals: to be absorbed completely into the life of a tribe while maintaining an objective, scientific eye; to write an ethnography, which by definition is an insider's account, that accurately describes and explains an "exotic" culture for outside Western observers; and to spend no more than two to five years doing the fieldwork necessary for such an ethnography before returning to an academic position in North America. In other words, to mimic Joseph Atkinson's prestigious career. Fieldwork is a "rite of passage," and if you can't make a success of it, you might as well "think about a nice career in sociology, where the data were unlikely to carry a spear" (48).

Martiya's own foray into anthropological fieldwork is not nearly as neatly scripted as Atkinson's. Having failed to reestablish contact with the village in which she grew up, she settles in with the Dyalo, an ethnic minority some one hundred thousand strong, spread across China, Burma, and the northern hills of Thailand. After three years, she returns to Berkeley, "tanned and strong," with her own "encrusted layers of culture and ingrained habit and prejudice" scoured away to reveal her authentic self (51). But her authentic self does not want to subject the Dyalo to an ethnographic study; it wants to understand them, to live with them. And so, against the advice of friends and mentors, Martiya abandons her doctoral thesis and returns to Thailand to live in the village of Dan Loi.

As she immerses herself in the life of the Dyalo, Martiya begins to understand one of their central ceremonies, *dyal,* a fertility ritual that guarantees a bountiful rice harvest. What at first appears to be a mysterious and taboo subject—the men of the village disappear, other men reappear, and everyone refuses to answer her questions about their movements—takes shape when Martiya discovers that during the week of planting, spouses are exchanged between villages. Husbands take a "wife" from another village, and wives are claimed by a "husband" from yet another. For some couples, these yearly trysts are treasured encounters—sanctioned affairs that reignite passion and love for both husbands; for others, they are the scene of an annual, and dreaded, rape. In an attempt to identify with her village, Martiya begins to participate in the rice festival, to practice *dyal,* only to discover that she has fallen in love with her *gai-kin,* her rice husband. Breaking all the rules of both the Dyalo and her anthropological discipline, Martiya and Hupasha, her *gai-kin,* continue to meet throughout the year. But when Hupasha becomes a Christian, an Adam-person, he forsakes not only the rice ritual itself but also his relationship with Martiya. It is a break that leads directly to the murder of David Walker.

As we accompany Mischa along the twists and turns of Martiya's life, we note, as he does, that anthropology's famed scientific objectivism is itself a form of faith with its own creed—merge with the people you are studying, but do not change them; its own rituals of participation; its own saints—the anthropologists who bring back the big stories; and its own cardinal sin—interfering with rather than describing another culture. Although Martiya herself breaks this great taboo, both by falling in love with Hupasha and by violating the code of Rice, she sees herself as a defender of the Dyalo. Her fierce desire to protect their traditional ways—and reclaim her lover—brings her into conflict with the Walker clan, who for four generations have been conducting their own fieldwork among the Dyalo.

In a nice pun, Berlinski converts Martiya's anthropological term *fieldwork* into the parlance of evangelical missionaries, as in "We'll be returning to the *field* later this month." Many evangelical Christians see missionary activity as a direct response to Jesus' words to his disciples: "Say not ye, There are yet four months, and then cometh harvest? behold, I say unto you, Lift up your eyes, and look on the fields; for they are white already to harvest" (John 4:35, KJV). Mischa, the narrator, finds himself even more intrigued by the missionaries than by the anthropologists. The latter fit into known categories of academics and expatriates— Americans living abroad—with whom he has some familiarity, but the former are totally exotic. Are the Walkers warlords? Philanthropists? Neocolonialists? Are they fabulously wealthy or as poor as the proverbial church mice? Do they live in a big house with many servants and tell people how to live, as Gunther the yoga teacher insists, or is Gunther mistaking them for his own reflection? "Gunther himself lived in a big house with many servants and told many people how they must live," Mischa tells us, "but it did not seem the right moment to mention that" (56).

The stories about the Walkers are "often improbable and sometimes mutually impossible" but Mischa hopes "they were all true" (57–58). What he discovers, after his initial visit to their "dingy" compound (59), is a large, four-generation family whose lives are "stranger, far stranger, than those who had traded rumors and spun idle gossip" could have imagined (58). This is a family from Oklahoma who speaks perfect Thai, Dyalo, and English; who bake sweet potato pie for Thanksgiving and make up pitchers of "cool orange Tang," but who also know how to exist on rice and roots. This is the solid Midwestern family who has called China, Burma, and Thailand home, who has visited Tibet by invitation of the Grand Tigi of Gartok, whose Aunt Helena married a Kachin evangelist, and whose reigning patriarch, Thomas, spent eighteen months in a communist prison for love of a Dyalo woman. This is the Bible-believing family who disdains movies and other trappings of Western culture and who seems unable even to imagine a perspective other than their own, but who sensitively translates Psalm 23 into the syllables and rhythms of Dyalo life:

> *I am Wu-pa-sha's* bi'na-ma; *there is nothing I want.*
> *He brings me to sleep in the soft grass of the green rice*
> *fields;*
> *He leads me to the clean water drinking spot.*
> *He brings me back my lost souls;*
> *He shows me good customs for his honor.*
> *Even though I walk through the valley of the shadow of*
> *death,*
> *I fear no bad spirits: because You are with me.* (287)

This is the family who scorns death but lives to convert the Dyalo to Christianity.

David Walker exemplifies all these apparent contradictions and more. Born in Burma and raised in Thailand, he returns to the States at age twenty, becomes a Deadhead for four years, and then one miraculous night hears Jerry Garcia strumming the same tune his grandfather had heard in a foxhole in France during World War I:

> *There were ninety-and-nine that safely lay*
> *In the Shelter of the fold.*
> *But one was out on the hills far away,*
> *Far off from the gates of gold.* (153)

And just like that, David packs his bags, returns as the prodigal son—or wandering sheep—to the pressure cooker embrace of his family, and begins his own career as an evangelist to the Dyalo.

By age thirty he is dead, shot twice in the back with Martiya's hunting rifle.

It is not by chance that the stories of Martiya and David converge in the fields of the Dyalo. *Fieldwork* is ultimately located in the literal field work that has given the Dyalo their name: the *dyal* fertility ceremony that placates the spirit of Rice and that brings Martiya into contact with her *gin-kai*, Hupasha, and the Walkers into conflict with the ideology that undergirds the ritual. In the end, the stories Martiya and the Walkers tell about themselves and about the Dyalo are incompatible. As Thomas Walker explains to Mischa: "The Dyalo would tell her that they were in bondage—*bondage!*—to the demons, and she'd write in her little notebook, 'The Dyalo have a rich hierarchical system of animistic spirit worship'" (72). The Dyalo, too, are divided. Hupasha genuinely believes that Christianity has freed him from demons, but others return to their traditional religion when the rice harvests begin to fail. What links the Walkers, Martiya, and the Dyalo themselves, however, is passionate belief—in God, in spiritual forces, in the rightness of their own perspectives, in love.

What are we as readers to make of these alternative visions? We may be drawn to Martiya's faith in observation and description, the discipline of anthropology to which she returns at the end of her life when she makes her ethnographic studies of the women at Chiang Mai Central Prison. Or we may find her more sympathetic when she abandons scientific objectivity to make forbidden love with Hupasha. We may be drawn to, or at least fascinated by (as Mischa the narrator is), the extended Walker family, with their myriad of aunts, uncles, and cousins, their utter certainty in their own vocation, their "enthusiasms and convictions" (133), their passion to preach the gospel—the first time in his life, Mischa notes wonderingly, that he had "heard anyone use the word 'preach' in a wholly literal sense" (62).

Or we may feel distanced from each of the characters. For all his wonder and curiosity, Mischa tells the stories of the Walkers and Martiya and the Dyalo dispassionately. At the very least, he is a narrator whose attention constantly strays and whose own identity wavers. He signs some of his articles with the pseudonym Somchai Wannapongsi in order to provide "an authentic voice of Asia" for the readers of an English-language Bangkok newspaper (21–22), and he slips into the cadences of whomever he is with. With Josh O'Connor, he is the brash expatriate; with Rachel, a befuddled lover; with Gunther, a yoga initiate. When he talks with the Walkers, he lapses uncharacteristically into silence, noting that "there was some weirdness in the Walker way that made the normal conversational forays seem weak and ineffective, even inappropriate. It was like talking to royalty, or to the very wealthy, or the very beautiful" (65). The novel, like the narrator himself, skitters across the surface of Southeast Asia. Characters wink in and out, as slapdash as the opium dream Mischa enjoys with Khun Vinai when he tracks down Martiya's last moments of freedom.

Perhaps it is the art of journalism itself that creates a disjointed and random narrative, or at least Mischa's somewhat dilettante view of that career. The journalist, Mischa notes, is little more than "the baton in a relay race of faulty memories and distant recollections" (35). Or perhaps the displacement of encountering another culture keeps intimacy at bay. Rachel and Mischa rear back "in lunatic miscomprehension" when Baiyom charges into their yard brandishing her machete (19), but even Martiya and the Walkers, who enter deeply into the life of the Dyalo, are often caught by surprise. It is Thomas Walker, whom his own mother calls a "green-eyed, blond-haired Dyalo boy" (119), who says, "We're not Dyalo, and God made people as mysterious as He is. You don't get to know anyone" (72).

Yet part of Mischa's fascination with the Walkers is the opportunity they present to get to know people who are completely different. They give him the chance to do his own fieldwork, his own anthropological investigation into the strange tribe known as Christian missionaries. He confesses, "I had grown up in Manhattan. The only serious Christian I had ever met was my co-op's handyman, a black man named Leon who was born again when I was about eleven. . . . The phrase 'born again' had confused me considerably at the time, and played on my imagination in horrific ways" (57–58). Now an adult, the promise of Christianity again plays on Mischa's imagination and around the edges of his soul. He finds it odd that despite their evangelistic fervor for the Dyalo, the Walkers don't try to convert him. And the oddness, we suspect, is not simply that this reticence seems to be inconsistent with their own beliefs, but also because Mischa would like to receive an invitation to come "inside," even if he declined it.

It is precisely such a withheld invitation that contributes to David Walker's murder. When Martiya comes to the Walker compound, distraught and displaced after Hupasha has abandoned her to take up Christianity, she asks to be baptized. But although Mrs. Walker offers her the obligatory cup of cold water that Jesus commanded his disciples to give to those in need, she refuses Martiya the water of baptism, the sign of conversion; she refuses because she suspects that Martiya has engaged not just her husband's intellect, but his affections. And just as Martiya's crucial decision to turn her back on her cherished anthropological creed by breaking the Rice taboo leads to the murder, so also does Mrs. Walker's crucial decision to turn her back on the Christian creed to love her enemy: "If you had done what any decent Christian woman would do," her husband accuses, "David would still be here today" (277).

To have a moral center is a precious gift and a terrible commodity. The Walkers' moral and spiritual center anchors them to God and to the Dyalo people despite death and loss and privation and exile. It is "the fundament, the support, the rainbow and reliable anchor that is the promise of God" (89), and abandoning that center even for an instant leads to murder. Martiya, too, suffers when she sacrifices her anthropological creed for the love of Hupasha, and although she returns to anthropology when she is in prison, it cannot sustain her beyond the completion of the two ethnographic studies. Mischa, on the other hand, seems to lack a moral center as he rushes chameleon-like from episode to episode in pursuit of his story.

But "center" is not actually the metaphor Berlinski employs to describe spiritual sensibilities in this novel, and it may not be the word we should use. Rather, he chooses a more mobile image, that of the pendulum. "Like so many occidentals in the Orient," Mischa says, "the Walkers had swung to the pendulum-edges of their souls" (107). And earlier Mischa notes that "in the leisure, freedom, and isolation that the Far East provides, [foreigners] swing inexorably toward the pendulum-edges of their souls" (21). A pendulum, of course, has a point of rest, an equilibrium position, a home. And it seems that all the characters in *Fieldwork* are searching for home. Martiya longs to recreate her cherished childhood in a small village, even to the point of accepting the reality of Rice and the spirit world; the Walker children resist going "home" to the States because, after a life of exile, China or Burma or Thailand seems more like their real home than does the country that holds their passport; the Walker parents talk of death as "going Home"; and Rachel pressures Mischa to move back home. But a pendulum is made to swing, its equilibrium point more a theoretical position than a resting place. And whether it is God or love or sexual desire or a good story or simply living in a foreign place that sets the pendulum in motion, once it begins to swing, the momentum will push the soul perilously close to the edge—of intensity, of hope, of sanity—but also toward belief.

Fieldwork may not probe the depths of faith and doubt, but by opening up a world in which spirits move freely, and anthropologists come to believe in Rice, and missionaries welcome home their prodigal sons, and a restless twentysomething is intrigued by Christianity, it reminds us, in Hamlet's words, that there are more things in heaven and earth than are dreamt of in our philosophy.

▌ Discussion Questions about the Novel

1. Mischa justifies his obsession with learning about Martiya by noting, "such is the power of a good story" (22). Is *Fieldwork* a good story or is it a collection of too many stories? Mischa the narrator excuses the proliferation of narratives by saying that "Thailand was full of strange stories and inexplicable mysteries" (31). But in the Acknowledgments the author notes that his editor "cut whole chapters" and once wrote "'No, no, no!' directly across the text" (319). Do you find yourself interested in the minor characters, or do Berlinski's descriptions of them become annoying or distracting? Do they add to the texture of the novel, or do they create a collage that dissipates the plot of the book?

2. Both Martiya and the Walkers are products of their history, and the novel spends a great deal of time narrating their past lives. How bound are we to tradition, to our families, to their choices and mistakes? What happens not just to us but also to others when we make a radical choice? When the Oklahoman Walkers decide to spend their lives in China; when the first Dyalo becomes an Adam-person; when Martiya decides to

live with Hupasha, what ripples do they create? Do each of these conversions have negative as well as positive results? Is damage inevitable?

3. *Fieldwork* begins with an epigraph from Freud: "The main achievement of religion, as compared with animism, lies in the psychic binding of the fear of demons. Nevertheless, the evil spirit still has a place in the religious system as a relic of the previous age." Do you think that "religion" contains and controls spirituality? Does this novel make you more or less ready to believe in supernatural powers?

4. Do you think that the final turning points of the murder plot—the love affair between Hupasha and Martiya and the emotional affair between Thomas Walker and Martiya—are believable? Has the author prepared us for love triangles in which God is the third person? Does the author prepare us for Martiya's request for baptism and Norma's refusal?

5. The narrator tells us that "the field did to Martiya what the field always does: it scoured her and revealed the person underneath the encrusted layers of culture and ingrained habit and prejudice" (51). Should we take this statement seriously, as a comment on the nature of human beings who consist of an inner authentic self and an outer husk of culture and prejudice? Or is this a false, or at least in-complete, notion of men and women? Do the cultures and prejudices that we are born into make us who we really are? Can we strip them away, or do we merely replace them with other cultures and prejudices that we assume or put on or convert into?

6. How do you respond to the author using his own name, Mischa Berlinski, as the name of the narrator? Does it make the story more immediate? More realistic as the report of a journalist? Or does it make you take both the narrator and novel less seriously? Were the references and footnotes— some fictitious and some factual—confusing or helpful?

▨ Other Books to Consider

—Wade Davis, *The Serpent and the Rainbow: A Harvard Scientist's Astonishing Journey into the Secret Societies of Haitian Voodoos, Zombies, and Magic.* New York: Warner Books, 1985.

An ethnographic study of Haiti that reads like a novel. Davis explores the roots of voodoo in African culture, its role in the Haitian independence movement, and its powerful presence in contemporary society.

—Alexandra Fuller, *Don't Let's Go to the Dogs Tonight: An African Childhood.* New York: Random House, 2001.

A memoir of growing up in Africa that evokes the smells, colors, and sounds of Rhodesia (now Zimbabwe), Zambia, and Malawi. Filled with a child's warm memories, it also evokes the turbulent decade of the 1970s, when even children learned to use Uzis, and the clash of colonial and native cultures turned increasingly violent.

—Isobel Kuhn, *By Searching.* London: Overseas Missionary Fellowship Books, 1957; and *Ascent to the Tribes: Pioneering in Northern Thailand.* London: Overseas Missionary Fellowship Books, 1956.

Classic missionary stories. The first is a memoir of the author's late adolescence and early adulthood that includes her return to her Christian faith and her decision to move to China as a missionary. The second details her life among the Lisu people before her early death from cancer.

—Gertrude Morse, *The Dogs May Bark: But the Caravan Rolls On*. Joplin: College Press, 1998.

Recommended by Berlinski as the book that provided much of the background for *Fieldwork*, this memoir of the Morse family follows their adventures as missionaries in Southeast Asia.

Integrative Discussion Questions for Part One

1. *Intuition* and *Fieldwork* both take us inside the working lives of professionals—research scientists in the case of *Intuition* and anthropologists and missionaries in the case of *Fieldwork*—but neither novel is written by insiders from those professions. Do you think they give an accurate view of what it means to be a scientist, or an anthropologist, or a missionary? Do they, in the case of the scientists and anthropologists, show what it might mean to use (or have faith in) the scientific method?

2. All three novels present characters who are confronted with the discrepancy between their ideals and the real world. What is a proper balance between being a realist and being an idealist? What are the dangers of leaning too far either way? Are there dangers in maintaining a perfect balance? How does looking at something through spiritual eyes veer us in one or the other direction?

3. In *March*, the title character, despite his best intentions, does great harm. In *Intuition*, good science goes bad. In *Fieldwork*, the desire for anthropological purity leads to murder. How are we to understand the unraveling of ideals and desires? Are we inevitably prone to obsessions and destruction? What checks and balances—in these novels and in our own lives—can prevent us from harming ourselves and others?

4. *Fieldwork*'s image of the pendulum is meant to suggest something true about the nature of human experience: we are, as Shakespeare noted, "to one thing constant never." How might Berlinski's pendulum be used to describe the meanings of *March* and *Intuition*? Do you think all three authors would agree on this description of human experience? Would their protagonists agree? Would you?

PART TWO

"Where the Grapes of Wrath Are Stored"

"Where the Grapes of Wrath Are Stored"

One of the questions that all writers ask of their manuscripts is this: what motivates my characters? The answer, of course, will determine how a character acts, how a character makes decisions and establishes relationships, how a character grows or fails to grow. One motivation that speaks to the presence of ideals in the world is, quite simply, pain. Pain and the response to it—both on the part of characters and readers—may well affect how ideals are realized, or negotiated, or compromised, or abandoned, or perhaps replaced.

It is not hard to find pain as a motivating factor. Do you like the great Victorian novels? Think of the pain of Miss Havisham that affects not only her life, but also threatens to thwart the life of Pip. Or the shame of Elizabeth Bennett when she realizes the justice of Mr. Darcy's rebuke of her family. Do you like children's novels? Think of the cast of characters who live in darkness in *The Tale of Despereaux*. Do you like science fiction? Consider the struggles of the father and son in Cormac McCarthy's *The Road*. Or the chilling effects on a colonized world in Ray Bradbury's *The Martian Chronicles*. Do you like realistic fiction? Think of John Updike's *In the Beauty of the Lilies*. Or of the struggle to forge an identity after losing one's own sense of self in Tom Wolfe's *I Am Charlotte Simmons*.

Whatever its origins—personal, cultural, political, relational, emotional—pain may shake, even obliterate ideals. The suffering and anger that arises from it may pressure any hope for the realization of any ideals. And since we do live in a world of pain, the question comes, how do we live with pain and yet avoid its debilitating effects? How do we live in a fallen world of suffering and still believe that ideals can exist at all?

These are the questions that Chimamanda Ngozi Adichie, Edward P. Jones, and Michael Chabon ask. They use different genres—a coming-of-age novelistic memoir, a historical novel about a fictional Virginia county, a hard-boiled detective story interlaced with science fiction and apocalypse—and they pose radically different answers. But each crafts memorable characters who grow, or fail to grow, through their suffering and who nudge us to consider our own responses to the troubling persistence of pain.

PURPLE HIBISCUS

Chimamanda Ngozi Adichie

(2003)

Synopsis

Growing up in modern Nigeria, fifteen-year-old Kambili faces a world filled with contrasts, a world where the Igbo language and English are spoken almost interchangeably, and where traditional religious practices continue alongside the Catholicism brought decades earlier by British colonists. Kambili's father, Eugene, is a successful businessman and the publisher of an independent newspaper. His wealth and influence keep the family safe during a military coup, but Eugene himself is violent and oppressive toward every member of his family, forcing them to practice a strict form of Catholicism and to speak no language other than English.

Kambili discovers a new kind of family dynamic when she and her brother visit their Aunt Ifeoma, a struggling university professor, and Ifeoma's three children. In Ifeoma's household, everyone talks to everyone else—in both Igbo and English, often at the same time. Ifeoma's family blends Catholicism with more traditional religious practices, and Kambili gains an appreciation for traditional music performed by modern artists. She learns respect for her pagan grandfather, and she develops a crush on a charismatic young priest named Father Amadi. The novel follows the growth of Kambili as she emerges from under the protective and oppressive authority of her father and begins to discover her own identity in a wider, more complex world.

On the Author

Chimamanda Ngozi Adichie was born in Nigeria in 1977 and grew up in Nsukka, living in a house formerly occupied by the author Chinua Achebe (whose famous novel *Things Fall Apart* receives a gentle nod in the first sentence of *Purple Hibiscus*). She moved to the United States to attend college at the age of nineteen, and she currently divides her time between the United States and Nigeria.

Purple Hibiscus was short-listed for the Orange Broadband Prize for Fiction and was awarded the Commonwealth Writers' Prize for Best First Book. Adichie has written one other novel, *Half of a Yellow Sun* (2006), also set in Nigeria.

Considering the Novel

Purple Hibiscus is the story of Kambili's coming of age as she escapes the harsh protection of her father and finds a voice of her own. The soft, vibrant flowers that give *Purple Hibiscus* its name also offer a visual metaphor for Kambili's growing maturity, her blossoming into a young woman. To Adichie's credit, however, *Purple Hibiscus* is not as simple as this symbol might suggest. The plot unfolds organically, and characters develop in surprising ways. The novel does not chronicle Kambili's growth in a straight line from bud to blossom, because few fifteen-year-olds mature according to any predictable schema.

The main themes of the novel are not about sights but sounds. Voices and languages are more prominent in the novel than flowers, and the interactions of these voices are more complicated than the simple image of the blossoming hibiscus. Even a quick glance at a random page from the book will reveal the italicized Igbo words in Kambili's world—words that Adichie rarely bothers to translate into English. Each of these two languages, moreover, teems with sublanguages: the language of the Catholic Church, the language of Papa-Nnukwu's religion, the "university talk" of Aunty Ifeoma (75), the pidgin English with which Jaja responds to the government inspectors (231). The central questions that Kambili faces throughout the novel are the questions of whether and how to respond to this cornucopia of languages and the experiences they each represent.

One possible response is dialogue: the act of answering another voice with a voice of one's own. Here, Aunty Ifeoma and her children seem to demonstrate the ideal way to inhabit the real world. Their home is filled with voices—voices that laugh and sing together, pray together, question one another, challenge one another. Sometimes the dialogue becomes so animated that it ceases to become a dialogue at all and unravels into a free-for-all. "Laughter floated over my head," says Kambili, recalling her time in Nsukka. "Words spurted from everyone, often not seeking and not getting any response. We always spoke with a purpose back home, especially at the table, but my cousins seemed to simply speak and speak and speak" (120). This lively atmosphere is well represented by Father Amadi, who speaks "English-laced Igbo sentences" on any number of topics: sports, politics, church activities, video games (135).

It is no accident that Amadi's first appearance in the novel shows him leading a worship service on the day of Pentecost, the holy day that commemorates the Holy Spirit's dramatic descent upon the fledgling Christian church in tongues of flame, mysteriously translating the preaching of the apostles into the native languages of everyone present (Acts 2). Appropriately, Father Amadi infuses the official Catholic liturgy for Pentecost with a song in Igbo.

As *Purple Hibiscus* celebrates dialogue, however, it also explores the disastrous alternatives to dialogue. It shows what happens to a dialogue when it is dominated by a single voice, and what happens when voices fall silent. Each of these alternatives is really one part of a dialogue taken to extremes. To truly participate in a conversation, a person must both speak and listen. A person who only speaks becomes selfish and domineering, like Eugene; a person who only listens becomes cowed and silent, like young Kambili. Eugene and Kambili's home is not completely without dialogue, but the potential dialogue there has been badly distorted and thrown out of balance. Eugene gets all of the words. A warm sharing of voices has degenerated into selfishness and silence.

Yet the sea of voices that characterizes Aunty Ifeoma's home in Nsukka also spills into Kambili's own home from time to time. Her mother's friends flood the house with Igbo songs during their praise sessions (21), and her mother herself sings Igbo songs on the last day of school (39). Once, a Pentecostal spirit even seems to visit the family dinner table:

> Papa read from the psalms before saying the Our Father, the Hail Mary, the Glory Be, and the Apostles Creed. Although we spoke aloud after Papa said the first few words alone, an outer silence enveloped us all, shrouding us. But when he said, "We will now pray to the spirit in our own words, for the spirit intercedes with us in accordance with His will," the silence was broken. Our voices sounded loud, discordant. Mama started with a prayer for peace and for the rulers of our country. Jaja prayed for priests and for the religious. I prayed for the Pope. Finally, for twenty minutes, Papa prayed for our protection from ungodly people and forces, for Nigeria and the Godless men ruling it, and for us to continue to grow in righteousness. Finally, he prayed for the conversion of our Papa-Nnukwu, so that Papa-Nnukwu would be saved from hell. (60–61)

Everyone is allowed to speak, and the multiple voices break free from the scripted words of the official prayers and creeds. Or do they? Even the allegedly spontaneous prayers of the different family members sound as if they have been ghostwritten by Eugene himself: they reflect his nationalist and religious values, and they are concerned entirely with men in higher positions of power. It is also worth noticing that Eugene's voice not only seems present in the prayers of his family, but his voice alone neatly frames all of their prayers. It is he who says the first few words alone, and it is he who gets the last word—twice. Adichie wryly suggests the tedium of his conclusion by beginning two sentences with the word *finally.*

It is perhaps tempting to think of Eugene as naively egocentric, unaware of speakers other than himself. But Eugene is quite aware of them. He does not ignore other voices, but overpowers them. The authoritarian atmosphere in his home comes about not through his ignorance but through his active suppression of other voices and languages. Eugene is bilingual, after all, and the one language that he chooses to speak—English—is not his cradle tongue. He speaks it not because he lacks other languages, but because he has deliberately chosen one to replace all others. Ironically, he criticizes Father Amadi's Pentecost sermon in terms that contradict the very spirit of Pentecost itself. "That young priest," he says, "singing in the sermon like a Godless leader of one of those Pentecostal churches that spring up everywhere like mushrooms" (29). Eugene's heart and soul simply have very little room for more than one language, more than one voice.

Eugene enters the story by launching a missal at his own son. His choice of projectile is significant. It is a book; he literally throws words at Jaja. Although Jaja successfully evades the attack, the other words that Eugene has fired at his children over the years have clearly affected them. When they speak, they frequently sound like their father. When Jaja learns that his mother is pregnant, for example, he says to Kambili, "We will take care of the baby; we will protect him" (23). Kambili immediately understands that Jaja means "protect him from Papa," but in the very act of resisting his father, Jaja adopts Eugene's tone of voice. He speaks with certainty and authority; he assumes that the baby will be male. We hear his father's voice in his.

In Kambili, the impact is even deeper. Eugene's voice does not merely appear in the tones of her speech; it seems to provide the exact words of her thoughts. At the parade with her grandfather, for example, she is told that women are not allowed to look at one particular *mmuo*. As she sorts through the ethics of this situation, Kambili repeatedly invokes terminology that echoes her father: "It was sinful, deferring to a heathen masquerade. But at least I had looked at it very briefly, so maybe it would technically not be deferring to a heathen masquerade" (86). Twice in Nsukka, she turns away from a naked family member because "it was sinful to look upon another person's nakedness" (117, 168). These are clearly Eugene's phrasings. In Jaja and Kambili's speech, we detect a form of verbal colonialism: Eugene governs the tones and sometimes even the actual words of his children's thoughts, replacing their natural instincts with his own.

This form of verbal colonialism is closely related to the ideas of political, religious, and cultural colonialism that run throughout the novel. As Aunty Ifeoma observes, Eugene himself is "too much of a colonial product" (13): he has allowed his words, his actions, and his very soul to be shaped by the foreigners who colonized Nigeria. He insists that English be spoken in public (13), and he even confesses his sins in English (104). In his absolute rule over his household, therefore, Eugene is effectively a middle manager between the early British colonists of Nigeria and his family. His Nigerian daughter thinks of God as a white man with a British accent (131, 179), a view imported and imposed on her without her permission or even her knowledge.

Eugene's strict control of every word in his household is one alternative to healthy dialogue, and it naturally provokes yet another alternative in his wife and children: silence. Their silence is not the deliberate active silence of meditation and monasticism, but the helpless, passive silence of those who have been shouted down. Eugene seems to speak with the voice of God, and once God has spoken, what more is there for mortals to say? In the wake of a military coup, Eugene lectures his family on the need for a "renewed democracy" in Nigeria. Kambili listens to him in passive reverence:

> *Renewed Democracy.* It sounded important, the way he said it, but then most of what Papa said sounded important. He liked to lean back and look upwards when he talked, as though he were searching for something in the air. I would focus on his lips, the movement, and sometimes I forgot myself, sometimes I wanted to stay like that forever, listening to his voice, to the important things he said. (25)

Ironically, a lecture on democracy completely erases Kambili's will to use her own voice.

For most of the novel, however, Kambili's silence is not the willing stillness of an attentive audience, but the restless longing of a person who needs to speak but has no voice. She and Jaja, for instance, have learned to communicate with one another silently on topics as varied as school lunches and their mother's well-being (22, 59). Kambili repeatedly listens to other people speaking, wishing that she could join the conversation, but when she does speak in public, she tends to stutter or cough. What makes this silence particularly painful for us as readers is Adichie's choice to write the novel in the first person. We experience the entire story from Kambili's perspective, so we are always aware that the speechless fifteen-year-old girl has a great deal that she wishes to say—she literally has an entire novel in her head. Silence is deadly: Kambili seems to be suffocating emotionally and socially because of her inability to speak.

Perhaps fittingly, Eugene himself falls into dead silence by the end of the novel. His tea has been laced with poison from "a powerful witch doctor" (290). The traditional religion that he so stridently suppresses ultimately provides the means for his demise. Similarly, the very stillness that he imposes on his wife and children seems to turn on Eugene, rising up in silent revenge. His wife, Beatrice, murders him without a word—even a word to us, the readers. We learn only at the end of the story that she has been poisoning him for much of the novel, conducting a silent revolution against the family tyrant. In fact, she acts very much like Eugene himself: her secrecy allows no opportunity for conversation, deliberation, or even collaboration. She simply does as she pleases. In a way, she is poisoning herself as well. In the final chapter of the novel, we learn that Beatrice has herself fallen into morbid silence, almost never initiating any form of conversation (306).

Eugene's outspoken domination is oppressive, and the silence it creates in his household turns out to be deadly even to him. He is a character of extremes: he owns either all the words or none of them. But Kambili's path clearly lies somewhere between these two extremes. Her challenge in the novel is to find her voice. The phrase "to find one's voice" is frequently used metaphorically to describe the work of musicians and writers, but in Kambili's case the challenge is also quite literal: she must learn to produce her own words with her own mouth. Given the idea of dialogue and its two alternatives—selfish outspokenness and silent submission—it would seem that the plot of the novel should be very straightforward: to grow out of her silence, Kambili must overcome or circumvent her father's powerful control without becoming an outspoken tyrant herself. She must join the healthy dialogue embodied by her aunt and cousins.

But the novel is not that simple. Adichie develops artful complexity in her characters and her plot. Kambili cannot merely maneuver away from her father toward her aunt because neither character occupies a fixed place on any moral or social map. Eugene rules the actions and even the thoughts of his family with ruthless rigidity, but he fearlessly advocates for democracy and free speech in a rapidly changing Nigeria. He physically abuses each member of his family, sometimes beating them within inches of their lives, but he also practices genuine charity. He lives up to the title of *omelora*, "The One Who Does for the Community," by generously dispensing money to the residents of Abba and feeding the entire village to "a reasonable level of satisfaction" (56). In addition to fulfilling this traditional role, he routinely gives cash to the poor in the streets (44) and he donates—anonymously— to several charitable organizations (297). He is fiercely loyal to his family, keeping Beatrice as his wife despite public pressure to send her away and marry someone else (20). In fact, it could be argued that the strength and determination that make Eugene so offensive are the same qualities that keep his family—including the extended clan in Abba—safe and well fed during politically dangerous times.

If Eugene exhibits, in some respects, the kind of generosity that we would more easily associate with his sister Ifeoma, the reverse is also true: Ifeoma shares her brother's strength of will and even some of his religious and moral commitments. Her home is not a place where anything goes. She is a committed Catholic who practices both morning and evening prayers (124, 126). She might tell Kambili that Papa-Nnukwu's ritual declaration of innocence is "the same as saying our rosary" (166), but she herself does not practice any of her father's rituals, so they are clearly not exactly the same to her. Ifeoma also believes in corporal punishment. She flogs Obiora for disrespecting a guest, and her disciplinary style—like Eugene's—features a strong educational component, a lengthy explanation of what is being punished and why (245).

In fact, the decisive moment when Kambili is snapped out of her silence comes not because of Ifeoma's easygoing hospitality, but because she scolds Kambili in a brief fit of frustrated anger. Amaka has yet again made a sniping comment at her quiet cousin, and Ifeoma lashes out at Kambili: "*O ginidi,* Kambili, have you no mouth? Talk back to her!" (170). Kambili does, in complete and articulate sentences, and even Amaka treats her differently for the rest of the novel. It is only when Ifeoma speaks like Eugene that Kambili can speak like Kambili.

Yet another complicated character is Father Amadi, the jack-of-all-trades who captures Kambili's heart. Like Ifeoma, he clearly enables Kambili to find her voice. Earlier in the novel, Kambili admits that she does not even know what her own laughter sounds like (88), but she finds out while driving with Amadi: "I laughed. It sounded strange, as if I were listening to the recorded laughter of a stranger being played back. I was not sure I had ever heard myself laugh" (179). On another drive with Father Amadi, Kambili first enjoys that other staple of the Nsukka crew—singing: "As we drove, we sang Igbo choruses. I lifted my voice until it was smooth and melodious like his" (239).

Achievements such as these, however, are overshadowed by unsettling questions. Amadi is a much older man, especially if age is measured not only in years but also in experience. Their inequality makes their relationship slightly troubling. Kambili, for example, might be said to be replacing her father with another authority figure (whose title happens to be "Father"). She is in the passenger seat not only literally but also metaphorically; a strong man is at the wheel. And although she seems to be finding her own voice, she is finding it by singing along with a tape, matching her voice to that of the driver. It is easy to imagine a Kambili a few years later whose thoughts and words contain fewer of her father's expressions and more of Father Amadi's.

Father Amadi's agenda in the relationship is also somewhat difficult to place. He does seem genuinely interested in almost everybody, but Kambili clearly occupies a special place in his heart. At times, this interest seems to move beyond outreach, sympathy, or even strong friendship. When he finds Kambili wearing wet *allamanda* flowers on her fingertips, for instance, he seductively slides one of the blossoms off her fingers and onto his own. "Is this the flower you can suck?" he asks. "The one with the sweet juices?" (269). His intentions in such scenes are unclear, perhaps even to himself. Amadi is an enigma, and his complicated relationship with Kambili helps to keep the novel from becoming a straightforward progression from silent submission to vocal freedom.

The plot of the novel also works against this linear progression. Its four sections are not arranged in chronological order, but begin in the middle of things, with the missal attack. Most of the novel is contained in the second section, "Speaking with Our Spirits: Before Palm Sunday," all of which leads up to the point at which the novel begins. Like a growing plant, the novel does not proceed in a straight line. And it extends further than we might expect. The third section, "The Pieces of Gods: After Palm Sunday," tells the aftermath of Eugene's initial outburst, resolving the central conflict of the novel. But there is more: the fourth and final section consists of a single chapter set in the present. Like Eugene himself, Adichie seems to need two finales. In this one chapter, however, the novel shifts from a story of adolescence to a story of adulthood.

It is a surprising chapter because of its restraint. It does not show Kambili happily married to Amadi. It does not show Jaja and the family reunited. It does not even show Kambili participating in the kind of dialogue toward which she seems to have been moving for the entire novel. In fact, the main representatives of that dialogue have moved to America and become somewhat dour and disillusioned. Even the silent conversations Kambili enjoyed with Jaja have become still; she wonders if the two of them had ever communicated in that way at all (305). In fact, the final chapter of the novel is in some ways so similar to earlier episodes that it feels more like the beginning of a story than the end. The purple hibiscus mentioned in Kambili's last speech, for instance, has not yet been planted. She looks forward to Jaja planting it in the future, and she concludes the book looking at the sky, anticipating "new rains" (307).

It might seem to some readers that the hopes they entertained for Kambili throughout the novel have been left unfulfilled. However, the final section shows what happens to childhood hopes in adulthood: some of them are made real, but in ways a child could not imagine. Kambili is, after all, confident. She still speaks very little, but she tends to initiate conversations instead of merely replying to other people, and several of her statements are imperative: she tells her mother to tighten her scarf; she tells the new driver to put a tape in the cassette deck (296, 297). In fact, she seems to be the one running the family's daily affairs. Earlier in the novel, readers eagerly await the time when Kambili finally outgrows her restrictive family, but in fact, the opposite happens: she grows into her family. She also seems to have more confidence in her personal life. She has not married Amadi, but neither is she devastated by unrequited love for him. Her love for him has matured into a more moderate form. "Amaka says people love priests because they want to compete with God," she says; "they want God as a rival. But we are not rivals, God and I. We are simply sharing" (303).

"Simply sharing" is a quiet, modest form of dialogue, and it is an action that is invested with spiritual significance in *Purple*

Hibiscus. It is noteworthy, for example, that Amadi is a living connection between Kambili and God. Kambili has come to think of God not as a white man shrouded in power and authority, but as an associate, a mutual shareholder in a community. Another example of simply sharing might well be the vision Kambili has of the Virgin Mary late in the third section of the novel: "And then I saw her, the Blessed Virgin: an image in the pale sun, a red glow on the back of my hand, a smile on the face of the rosary-bedecked man whose arm rubbed against mine. She was everywhere" (274–75). Kambili has developed a religious sensibility that combines the folk traditions of her grandfather with the Catholic iconography of her father. It is doubtful whether Eugene would call this an authentic vision of the Blessed Mother, and it is doubtful whether Papa-Nnukwu would see the point of using Mary's name to describe the vision. Kambili, however, draws from both traditions.

In fact, the final chapter shows us a Kambili who seems to have a healthy balance of silence, authority, and dialogue. She remains relatively quiet, but she is able to speak with certainty and authority when appropriate. And she has found her own form of dialogue, as well: not the noisy and exuberant tones that filled Ifeoma's house in Nsukka, but a calm capacity to entertain multiple voices in a spirit of simple sharing.

Discussion Questions about the Novel

1. Names are important in *Purple Hibiscus*. Ifeoma gets her name from Adichie's own mother (see the dedication). Jaja is the name of an Opobo king who defied the British colonialists (144), a clear forebear to the young man who defies his father's will in the first pages of the novel. Given the significance of names in the novel, what do you think

of Amaka's refusal to choose an English saint's name—
effectively a refusal to join the Catholic church? Is she
being too fussy, or is she taking an important stand?

2. Kambili's confirmation name, chosen by her father, is Ruth
    (204). What significant similarities do you see between
    Kambili and the biblical Ruth?

3. Papa-Nnukwu "knew that the white man was mad" when he
    first learned the doctrine of the Trinity, because that doctrine
    says that "the son and father are equal" (84). He is clearly
    disappointed that his own son, Eugene, fails to recognize his
    authority as the patriarch of the family. What do you think
    Eugene would say about the relationship of a father to his
    son, both in terms of the Trinity and in terms of his own son,
    Jaja? Does he seem to believe, as Papa-Nnukwu charges, that
    fathers and sons are equal?

4. Christian holidays are important to the story. Major plot
    developments happen on or around Easter, Pentecost, and
    Christmas. How does the religious significance of these holi-
    days relate to themes being worked out in the plot? Why is
    Palm Sunday the pivotal day around which the entire novel is
    organized?

5. In terms of religious practices, Kambili finds at least three
    options: her grandfather's traditional ideas and rituals, her
    father's orthodox Catholicism, and her aunt's attempt to
    blend the two. Which of these options seemed most and least
    promising to you? What are the dangers of each option?

6. Why are Beatrice's figurines of ballerinas referred to as
    "gods"?

7. Kambili first truly speaks up for herself when Aunty Ifeoma shouts at her, commanding her to do it. It is only when Ifeoma speaks like Eugene that Kambili can speak like Kambili. This episode raises an interesting question: must freedom of speech be enabled by authoritarian means? Would the *Standard* survive as a dissident voice without the monomaniacal zeal of Eugene?

Other Books to Consider

—Christopher Abani, *Grace Land*. New York: Farrar, Straus, and Giroux, 2004.

Elvis Oke comes of age in a ghetto in Lagos, Nigeria, in the 1970s and '80s. He loses his mother when he is just a boy and grows into a hardened young man—an Elvis impersonator—under the thumb of a drunken father and surrounded by influences ranging from traditional Igbo rituals to American popular culture.

—Chinua Achebe, *Arrow of God*. London: Heinemann, 1964.

The novel tells the story of Ezeulu, an Igbo chief priest in Nigeria, and his strained negotiations with British colonists and missionaries who arrived in the 1920s.

—Sefi Atta, *Everything Good Will Come*. Northampton, MA: Interlink Books, 2005.

The coming-of-age story of Enitan Taiwo, a Yoruba woman from Nigeria who is raised in an upper-middle-class home, but becomes a political activist after witnessing violence and experiencing oppression in her own country.

—Mary Karr, *The Liars' Club: A Memoir*. New York: Ecco Press, 1993.

Karr's memoir of her East Texas childhood is alternately hilarious and devastating as she copes with unstable parents and her own too perceptive sensibilities.

THE KNOWN WORLD Edward P. Jones
(2003)

Synopsis

Henry Townsend was born into slavery in Manchester County, Virginia. Lucky to work as a groom rather than a field hand, he makes himself indispensable to his master, William Robbins, who eventually develops a strong attachment to him. Robbins trains Henry in the "business of mastering" so that he can move into the white world of power and property. When Henry's parents finally are able to buy his freedom, he saves up his money and buys his own land and his first slave, Moses. While this act devastates his parents, moving from slave to slave owner seems only "natural" given the guidance Henry received from Robbins.

Henry comes to own thirty-three slaves and more than fifty acres of land. When he dies suddenly, the running of the estate falls to his wife, Caldonia, a freeborn black woman whose family also owned slaves. However, Caldonia is unable to run the Townsend estate with the same success as Henry had. A series of decisions, prompted by her grief, causes a chain of unforeseen events with profound consequences for all.

On the Author

Edward P. Jones (b. 1951) was born in a segregated neighborhood of Washington, DC, where he was raised by his single mother, who could not read or write. He was the first person in his family to go to college, attending Holy Cross College and the University of Virginia. He worked for two decades as a proofreader and news summarizer for *Tax Notes,* a professional journal, before being laid off in 2002. Losing his job pushed him to write *The Known World.* While he was already the author of the much-acclaimed *Lost in the City* (1992), a collection of short stories that won the Hemingway Foundation/PEN Award and a $50,000 literary prize, Jones had never wanted to be a professional writer; his years of living in poverty and watching his mother struggle taught him that a steady paycheck was a godsend.

Although Jones says that he had been working on *The Known World* "in his head" for about ten years, he completed the first draft of the novel within three months of losing his job. *The Known World* went on to win the Pulitzer Prize and the National Book Critics Circle Award in 2004, and was a finalist for the National Book Award. Jones continues to live in Washington, DC. His second collection of short stories, *All Aunt Hagar's Children,* was published in 2006.

Considering the Novel

Near the end of *The Known World,* when Barnum Kinsey, "the poorest white man in the county," finally tells Sheriff John Skiffington that Augustus Townsend, Henry's father, has been sold to a slave speculator, he reveals his own longing for the "lantern of truth":

> "A body should be able to stand under some . . . some kinda light and declare what he knows without retribution. There should be some kinda lantern, John, that we can stand under and say, 'I know what I know and what I know is God's truth,' and then come from under the light and nobody make any big commotion bout what

> he said. He could say it and just get on about his busi-
> ness, and nobody would say, 'He be stickin up for the
> nigger, he be stickin up for them Indians.' The lantern
> of truth wouldn't low them to say that. There should be
> that kinda light, John." (303)

Although we have longed for Barnum to do what is right since the night Augustus was kidnapped and sold to Darcy, we also know that his logic about the lantern of truth, although admirable in some ways, is flawed. Barnum implies that he could have told Skiffington the truth earlier if there had been a light that would allow him to "say what is" without fear of repercussions, but what he doesn't realize—or doesn't acknowledge—is that he has light enough already. When Barnum goes home that night, we read that he "could see a burning lamp on the table he and his family had their meals on. He saw two more on the mantelpiece, and when he turned around in that room, he saw his wife, and the two lamps on the mantelpiece were reflected in her eyes" (304). These lamps suggest that there is light enough in our lives already to "say what is" and that the lamps burning on a family table or in a loved one's eyes are more real and significant than any magic lantern, and provide sufficient motivation to tell the truth. Such truth, however, never comes without repercussions, nor is the truth that one knows always God's truth as well.

Indeed, religious justifications for the system of slavery—defined as God's truth—are peppered throughout the novel. For example, God is credited for generously providing the perfect weather for the buying and selling of slaves (8); Skiffington believes that slavery is an institution sanctioned throughout the Bible; when Henry talks about the future as he courts Caldonia, he says that "he would be a master different from any other, the kind of shepherd master God had intended" (180). Similarly, many of the characters also justify their actions by saying they are acting within the law. Most telling, when Fern is interviewed by Mr. Frazier, the pamphleteer, she explains, "All of us do only what the law and God tell us we can do. No one of us who believes in the law and God does more than that. Do you, Mr. Frazier? Do you do more than what is allowed by God and the law? . . . We owned slaves. It was what was done, and so that is what we did" (109). Even as she says this, however, the narrator tells us a different story of what is: "Fern looked down into the palm of her hand. Had Anderson not been white and a man . . . Fern might have opened up to Anderson. *This is the truth as I know it in my heart*" (109). The first truth that Fern tells is that slavery is sanctioned by God and the law, and thus it is not an "oddity" for free blacks to own black slaves. But the narrator implies that the truth as she knows it in her heart may be entirely different and may, in fact, exceed what corrupt laws made to reinforce slavery allow.

Part of the richness of *The Known World* comes precisely from this problem of watching likeable, upstanding, even moral characters do things that are despicable without even being aware of what they have done. The prime example of this is Henry Townsend himself. Augustus and Mildred Townsend, his parents, believe so strongly in freedom that they are willing to risk their own lives for the freedom of others. They believe that the evil of slavery is so obvious that they don't need to teach that truth to their son. When Augustus asks Henry why he doesn't know that slavery is wrong, he says "Why should anybody haveta teach you the wrong, son? . . . Ain't you got eyes to see it without me tellin you?" (137). The problem is that Henry's eyes tell him a different story. Henry truly believes that he *can* be a different kind of master, that it is possible to be a good master to slaves as opposed to an oppressive one. The narrator tells us that "Henry had always said that he wanted to be a better master than any white man he had ever known. He did not understand that the kind of world he wanted to create was doomed before he had even spoken the first syllable of the word *master*" (64). Similarly, Caldonia, when faced with the opportunity to free all of Henry's slaves, is described as being unable to "see any of those thirty or so human beings living as free people" (291). It would seem, then, that the characters of the novel can only operate within the world that they know. And sadly, any known world that includes slavery will come to corrupt all its members, the just and the unjust alike.

Henry, having grown up under the tutelage of William Robbins, lives in a world in which one can choose between various modes of mastering. Not recognizing the evil that slavery is in and of itself, Henry does not see the inevitable slide away from his initial dream of being the kind of master that God intended. Two days after Henry's funeral, Caldonia considers what kind of master he had been:

> Henry had been a good master, his widow decided, as good as they come. Yes, he sometimes had to ration the food he gave them. But that was not his fault—had God sent down more food, Henry would certainly have given it to them. Henry was only the middleman in that particular transaction. Yes, he had to have some slaves beaten, but those were the ones who would not do what was right and proper. Spare the rod . . . the Bible warned. Her husband had done the best he could, and on Judgment Day slaves would stand before God and testify to that fact. (181)

In some ways, Caldonia is right that Henry was "as good as they come," but that still isn't saying much because masters don't come very good. Her own assessment reveals that he was not living up to his claim that he would provide "good food for his slaves, no whippings, short and happy days in the fields" (180). Perhaps the starkest example of Henry's inability to redeem an evil system is his punishment of Elias when Elias attempts to run away. As he has tea and bread on a Sunday afternoon with the Reverend Moffett and Caldonia, he continues to engage in pleasantries while simultaneously musing in his head how much of Elias's ear he should have cut off. The supposed gentility of afternoon tea is put in sobering relief to Henry's cold calculations of "the whole ear or only a piece, and if a piece, how big a piece?" (89). Ultimately, we are allowed to see Henry's final reward in heaven. He is not rewarded by God with a cloud of slave witnesses testifying to his goodness as Caldonia had supposed. Instead, he "walked up the steps and into the tiniest of houses, knowing with each step that he did not own it, that he was only renting. He was ever so disappointed" (11).

Winifred Skiffington is another example of the ways in which the system of slavery corrupts all who touch it. Winifred had come from Philadelphia and hoped that she and John Skiffington would move back there some day. Her sister-in-law Belle gives her a slave, Minerva, "festooned with a blue ribbon," as a wedding gift. At first Winifred tells John that "slavery was not something she wanted in her life" (33). But when John, fearing the political consequences to his job as sheriff if his wife turns down the gift of a slave, convinces her that Minerva "might be better off with us than anywhere else. . . . Are you and me not good people?" Winifred relents. And, in fact, John and Winifred do treat Minerva better than most slaves in the county.

But here again we see the same problem in logic from which Henry suffered: the system of slavery is itself evil and, thus, there is no possibility of being a "good master." Winifred is slowly and imperceptibly influenced by her fifteen years living in the South. When she and Minerva, whom she has come to see as her daughter, finally move to Philadelphia after John's death, Minerva goes missing one day. A frantic and desperate Winifred has a printer make posters in an effort to find her. Minerva herself even sees the posters but decides not to return home to Winifred because written on the bottom of the poster, "like some kind of after-thought . . . was the line 'Will Answer to the Name Minnie'" (381). The narrator explains that Winifred had not meant any-thing bad by the line and that, in fact, she meant "only love." Unfortunately, living in the South, owning a slave, no matter how well she treated her, caused Winifred to continue to think of Minerva as less than white, less than human. "Will Answer to the Name Minnie" echoes the beginning of the novel, when Belle first gave Minerva to Winifred. Belle had told Winifred that Minerva would "answer to the name Minnie, but her proper name is Minerva. She will, however, answer to either, to what-ever you choose to call her," suggesting both that Minerva is like a dog who will answer to a different name and that Winifred is within her rights to change Minerva's name on a whim (32). In this scene at the novel's beginning, it is easy to see that Belle is a typical racist slaveholder and that Winifred is, by contrast, the enlightened Northerner. But by the novel's end, even without knowing it, even while performing an act of deep love, Winifred has moved to Belle's position as well.

If the most likable or sympathetic characters are revealed to be tragically flawed time and time again and limited in their vision of the world, is *The Known World* meant to convey the idea that morality is impossible to grasp because there is no place from which to view what is truly right and truly wrong? No place from which to be able to say with confidence, "I know what is and what I know is God's truth"? On the contrary, Jones is careful to show that there *is* such a place, a perch high enough from which to judge and a light bright enough to stand under. In a 2003 in-terview with Jeffrey Brown for PBS, Brown asked Jones why the reader is allowed to see the future of the characters before that future is arrived at. Jones said, "I was a kind of god, you know. I can see the day they're born. I can see the day they're born, I can see the day they will die." Jones explained that his need to tell the full story of his characters had to do with a matter of justice: "I'm not saying that [I am a kind of god] in any sort of lofty sense, but only I think in a need to be complete, to set the record straight, you know, the entire record straight, to be as whole as I possibly could." Whereas Barnum's attempt to set the record straight about what happened to Augustus fails because of his limited perspective on the consequences of his silence, Jones the writer feels that he can and should set the record straight for the characters of the world he has created. The characters' knowledge of their worlds is incomplete, but Jones is able to know that world to its very limits.

Furthermore, this is a knowledge that Jones shares, thus allowing readers to participate in the redemptive work of setting the record straight. A major feature of the novel is the tendency of the story to jump forward and backward in time rather than progressing in a linear fashion from start to finish. One wonderful example of this technique is the long scene in which Stamford, one of Henry's slaves who no longer has any "young stuff" to keep him young, decides that he might as well be dead. After Delphie explains in no uncertain terms that "[she] would not ever be with [him]," a fierce storm whips up. As Stamford wanders almost senselessly through the storm, he watches a bolt of lightning strike a large oak tree, instantly setting it ablaze and killing two crows. As Stamford looks at the crows and tries to steal some of their death for himself, the narrator describes a strange, almost mythic ritual that Stamford performs. As the ritual concludes, "he rubbed the yolks over their bodies. And when he was done, the ground opened up and took the birds in. He cried" (205). But the next paragraph abruptly begins by reporting that "this was the beginning of Stamford Crow Blueberry, the man who went on with his wife to found the Richmond Home for Colored Orphans" (205). We learn later that his wife is none other than Delphie.

This sudden jump to an improbable and unexpected happy ending for Stamford, an ending in which he has not only lived to a ripe old age but has also married and gone on to do great works of social justice, doesn't fit with the way in which the passage had been proceeding up to that point. From what we know of Stamford, the self-centered lothario of the Townsend plantation, and the kind of magical realism that occurs throughout the novel, we expect that Stamford will wander off and die without his young stuff and, if anything, his ritual with the crows is only his final recognition that he has been deluded and his life is without meaning. But this is not the case. Jones steps back to show us the true limits of Stamford's world and reveals that he does not die at a blasted oak tree but that he is born again as "Stamford Crow Blueberry," a great humanitarian in Richmond. The narrator sets the record straight and lets us say that we know what is, and what we know is God's truth.

Jones's claim to be like God and its implications for us as readers are appealing. His claim that he can see the whole lives of his characters in one moment, like a god, works to assure us that there is some higher power watching over the people of the novel, someone who does not want to mislead us but rather wants "to set the record straight." Therefore, we think, we can trust that while characters in the novel may be equally sure of what is right and are yet misguided, Jones will not misguide us as his narrator tells their story. Such a promise is reassuring in a novel that deals with the great human tragedy that is the history of slavery in the United States. Indeed, Jones's choice to write about black slave owners can also be seen as a kind of setting the record straight—most readers have probably never heard of black masters.

But Jones's claim poses a problem, too. Jones does know his fictional world and its limits, but he addresses a real-world problem and a historical period in his book. Can Jones know the real world as completely as his created one? Can he really set the record straight? There is a danger in mistaking Jones's authority in the fictional world for an equal level of authority in the real world—where Jones himself is only one voice—however much we agree with Jones's assessment of slavery and its more insidious corruptions. Such a confusion of Jones's authority of his fictional world with his authority in the real world is like Barnum's admirable yet still confused desire for a magic lantern that would guarantee that one could tell the truth without fear of retribution. However, rather than suggesting that we can never claim to be able to judge the right and wrong of any situation or, worse, that from a high enough perspective, slavery might not be so bad after all, the reader's recognition that Jones as author can see full lives in a single moment of his characters roots the knowledge of right and wrong—of good and evil—back in the world of family dinner tables, simple meals, and the lights reflected in a loved one's eyes.

In claiming that an author has a godlike position over his or her work, Jones suggests that there is a redemptive power in art, and it is with this idea that he closes his novel. *The Known World* ends with a letter from Calvin to Caldonia. Caldonia has long since married Louis, William Robbins's son, and Calvin has left Virginia for New York. He writes to his sister about an amazing work of art that he finds hanging in a room next to the saloon in which he had been drinking. He tells his sister, "It is, my Dear Caldonia, a kind of map of life of the County of Manchester, Virginia. But a 'map' is such a poor word for such a wondrous thing. It is a map of life made with every kind of art man has ever thought to represent himself. . . . It is what God sees when He looks down on Manchester" (384). The creator of this wondrous map is Alice Night, the same "crazy Alice" who was one of Henry Townsend's slaves and whom Moses sent out on a fool's errand with his wife and son when he decided they were an impediment to his future with Caldonia.

Alice has also made a map of the Townsend plantation, and "again, it is what God sees when He looks down" (385). Calvin then describes in gorgeous detail how the map, almost quiltlike in the way it has pieced together the lives of everyone who had ever lived or died on the plantation, has compressed time into a single moment represented on the single field of the map. Calvin says that "each person's face, including yours, is raised up as though to look in the very eyes of God. I look at all the faces and I am more than glad now that I knew the name and face of everyone there at your home. The dead in the cemetery have risen from there and they, too, stand at the cabins where they once lived" (385). Looking at the map, in which every person's face is raised to look into the very eyes of God, puts Calvin in God's position. All eyes look to him, and he can see both past and present on the plantation in perfect detail. Being in this vantage effects a moral transformation in Calvin. Previously, Calvin had been a character who longed to free slaves and to work with abolitionists, but he lacked the courage of his convictions and never acted. As a compensatory gesture, Calvin at least learned the names of all of Henry's slaves. This one simple act of affording Henry's slaves human dignity is what allows him to look down from God's vantage and to be undone by what he sees. Calvin writes:

There are matters in my memory that I did not know were there until I saw them on that wall. I must tell you, dear Caldonia, that I sank to my knees. When I was able to collect myself, I stood and found not only Priscilla watching me but Alice as well. . . . What I feared most at that moment is what I still fear: that they would remember my history, that I, no matter what I had always said to the contrary, owned people of our Race. I feared that they would send me away, and even as I write you now, I am still afraid. (386)

Alice's amazing map, what God sees when He looks down, cuts Calvin to the quick and reveals the truth that he has always known. He recognizes that even though he sought to be a good person within the institution of slavery, such a person cannot exist, and at the end of the day, he, too, owned other humans.

This is one twist in the story that Jones has not let us see beforehand. Perhaps it is because this scene comes to us in the form of a letter that Calvin has written to Caldonia, and Jones wants to allow Calvin to tell his own story of transformation. It is also unclear whether or not Calvin's impassioned letter to Caldonia will have any effect on her, she who remains on the plantation and still owns all of Henry's slaves. The one hint that a moral shift might occur in Caldonia's heart happens when she goes out to read Calvin's letter at Henry's grave. As she returns to the house, Caldonia sees Moses limping back to his cabin. The narrator tells us that "her heart stopped. Even years after their last encounter, her heart stopped. Moses did not look her way. She found it difficult to move after seeing him" (387).

Moses's hobbling at the hands of the county slave patrollers is a travesty of justice. It is certainly a false justice because the white patrollers do it on false pretenses and for no other reason than to see Moses suffer. But it is false justice in another sense as well. Over the course of the novel, Moses has gone from being a sympathetic character, a man who cannot figure out why God would "put black people to owning their own kind" (9), to a man driven by desperation, jealousy, and hatred. When he becomes Caldonia's lover, he imagines that she will soon free him and then marry him so that he can become the new Mr. Townsend, owner of the plantation and all the slaves therein. Moses's desire to rule over the other slaves causes him to develop a plan to send Alice, Priscilla, and his son to their deaths under the guise of having Alice take them to freedom.

This grievous betrayal, along with his many other petty deeds, might make Moses's hobbling seem like poetic justice—Moses gets what he deserves for trying to do away with his family and for wanting to become the new master. But here again Jones is careful to explain that there can be no justice in slavery's poisoned system. We are taught that the call of power over other slaves is a heady one when even Elias agrees to become the new overseer. Against the pleas of his beloved wife, Elias steps into Moses's vacated position and tells himself that it is so he can make things easier for his family. But accepting the job and becoming a tool for the master causes Elias to lose his sense of right. As the patrollers hobble Moses, Elias wonders "how had he come to forget just where he was in the world?" (373). So if even Elias, who started with the best of intentions and without meaning to do harm, became the instrument of injustice, Moses's fall is not simply a result of a flaw in his character but rather a consequence of the ways in which slavery perverts everything.

Furthermore, even if Moses did deserve some kind of punishment for the betrayal of his family, it is clear that hobbling is a punishment far too brutal and inhuman to inflict upon anyone. Oden Peoples, the Cherokee slave patroller whose side job is cutting ears and slicing tendons for masters wishing to punish their rebellious slaves, is sickened by what happens to Moses, an act that Oden himself has done. In Jones's understated, yet eloquent, style, the narrator explains that "Oden would never put his knife to a man again. It was one thing to cut a man, collect money for a job well done and go home and sup with his family. It was another to ride a long way with the man at his back, agonizing all the way in Oden's ear, the man's arms around Oden's waist" (376). Even the man with a heart so hardened that he cuts people for a living cannot stomach the hard reality of Moses's fate.

The tragedy of Moses's fate—both the deeds he is driven to and their terrible results—are captured in the simple scene of Moses limping back to his empty cabin, rendering Caldonia unable to move. Perhaps her heart has stopped because after reading Calvin's letter she realizes her own hand in what has happened to Moses? Perhaps she cannot move because she, too, has been transfixed by the revelation of Alice's map, just as Calvin has been? Or perhaps she simply pities Moses and is irritated by the reminder of their affair? But by the dwindling daylight in which Caldonia is suspended, and by Jones's rendering of that light in his book, we have enough light to see what is and to say what is God's truth.

Discussion Questions about the Novel

1. *The Known World* takes place in a world in which the narrator is just as likely to report that the Otis boys burst spontaneously into flames as to describe the food served at a dinner party. Why do you think Jones includes so many fantastical details or stories and presents them in such a matter-of-fact way? Are these meant to be comic relief in the midst of a dark novel? Or do they function in other ways?

2. At times the novel seems to suggest that Henry's desire to be a slave owner is a result of his "being raised" by William Robbins. At other times it suggests that Henry has a more

profound flaw, present since birth. Why do you think Henry wants to own slaves and be the kind of master that "God intended"? In other words, is Henry a product of nature or nurture?

3. Fern is a formidable woman who does not suffer fools gladly, and yet she seems to have a remarkable capacity for self-delusion. At the dinner party in which Fern talks about the abolitionist pamphlet she received, she says she has chosen sides in the cause of slaves against masters. What reasons does she give for her choice? Do those reasons strike you as weak ones or legitimate? True or false? Do you think she has come to see the truth about herself in that moment?

4. When Louis proposes to the widowed Caldonia, he says, "I never thought I was worthy of you." To which she replies, "We are all worthy of one another." What do you think Caldonia means by that? Who are the "we" that she is talking about?

5. After Counsel Skiffington's slaves and family all die of small-pox in a Job-like totality and he burns his house to the ground, Counsel embarks on a rather fantastical journey across the United States to Texas and then back to Virginia. Why does Jones have Counsel encounter so many odd people and places? Who is the mysterious band of people he meets in Texas? Do you end up feeling sympathetic for Counsel and his loss? What does it mean for us, as readers, to feel sympathy for a racist slaveholder? Does Counsel's journey change him or not?

6. When Alice makes her wondrous map of Manchester County and the Townsend Plantation, she transforms something evil and ugly into something beautiful. Does this mean that art can

transform anything? Everything? Are there some things that should not be the basis for a novel or turned into poetry?

▨ Other Books to Consider

—Octavia E. Butler, *Kindred*. Garden City, NY: Doubleday, 1979.

> A woman from the twentieth century, Dana, is brought back in time by her slave-owning ancestor Rufus when his life is endangered. Dana chooses to save him, knowing that her actions will cause a freeborn black woman to become his slave and, eventually, her grandmother.

—Charles Johnson, *Middle Passage*. New York: Atheneum, 1990.

> Rutherford Calhoun is a newly freed slave living in New Orleans in 1830. When he hops onto a boat leaving the harbor in order to escape a schoolteacher who wants to marry him, he discovers the boat is a slave rigger heading for Africa. Because his master had educated him, Calhoun becomes the captain's cabin boy in order to survive.

—Toni Morrison, *Beloved*. New York: Alfred A. Knopf, 1987.

> Morrison's now-classic story of Sethe, an escaped slave who chooses to cut her own baby daughter's throat rather than have her fall back into slavery.

—Sherley A. Williams, *Dessa Rose*. New York: W. Morrow, 1986.

> When Dessa attacks her master for killing her husband, she is sold to a slave trader. When she escapes, she comes to live with a white woman on an isolated farm, and the two develop a rich and complicated relationship that causes Dessa to question her original plans to escape to the West.

THE YIDDISH POLICEMEN'S UNION Michael Chabon
(2007)

Homicide detective Meyer Landsman is a man down on his luck. His career is a mess, his personal life is a wreck, and his alcoholism is uncontrolled. Landsman lives in a seedy motel called the Zamenhof in the federal district of Sitka, a temporary safe haven for displaced Jews in Alaska created by the U.S. government after the Holocaust and the collapse of the State of Israel in 1948. And to make matters worse, a crime has been committed on his watch: one of his neighbors, a mysterious former chess prodigy, has just been found murdered in a room down the hall. As Landsman begins to investigate the case out of an obligation created by proximity, it becomes clear that the higher-ups want the matter dropped immediately. Yet Landsman and his half-Tlingit partner, Berko Shemets, continue the investigation and eventually discover that the murder victim is Mendel Shpilman, the son of the leader of the Verbover, a group of Hasidic Jews who are also an organized crime ring, and Sitka's most powerful mob boss. Mendel had been believed by many to be the messiah who would restore Israel. However, though Mendel was known for performing miracles, he had not worn the mantle of "messiah" lightly, and he had fled from his family on his wedding night.

As Meyer, Berko, and Meyer's ex-wife, Bina Gelbfish, try to discover how Mendel went from hoped-for messiah to murdered heroin junkie, their investigations are set against the imminent return of Sitka to American rule, an ominous ticking clock that inspires sometimes hope, sometimes dread, sometimes apathy for the denizens of Sitka, as each contemplates life beyond its frozen borders, with no Jewish homeland.

On the Author

Michael Chabon (b. 1963) grew up in Pittsburg and Maryland. He realized he wanted to be a writer at the tender age of ten and devoured mysteries, ghost stories, detective fiction, and pulp fiction of all kinds. He attended the MFA program at the University of California, Irvine, and submitted a novel for his master's thesis that was a coming-of-age story set in Pittsburg, inspired in equal measure by F. Scott Fitzgerald and Philip Roth. Unbeknownst to him, Chabon's thesis advisor sent a copy of the thesis to his literary agent and the rest, as they say, is history. Chabon's thesis became the international bestseller *The Mysteries of Pittsburg* (1988). His critically acclaimed *The Amazing Adventures of Kavalier and Clay* was published in 2000 and won the Pulitzer Prize for Fiction in 2001. *The Yiddish Policemen's Union* was published in 2007 and won two prestigious science fiction awards for best novel, the Nebula and the Hugo. The novel was also nominated for an Edgar Award for best novel, a Sidewise Award for Alternate History, and was short-listed for the British Science Fiction Association Award for Best Novel. Chabon currently lives in Berkeley, California, with his wife, Ayelet Waldman, and their four children.

Considering the Novel

The Yiddish Policemen's Union is a tale of desperation, longing, and redemption tied up in a hard-boiled detective story set in Alaska. Chabon presents us with an alternative history in which a district in Alaska has become a Yiddish-speaking settlement for Jewish refugees from World War II. As such, the novel is at once both an exploration of the themes of Jewish identity and what it means for Jews who do or do not desire to return to their "homeland," as well as a romping mixture of detective fiction, science fiction, and love story.

At the center of this mix is Meyer Landsman—a man literally without a home. He lives at a hotel, which is by definition not a home because it is meant to be a place of temporary lodging; he is separated from his wife because of his guilt over his decision to abort their child, thus destroying their family unit; he has become increasingly incompetent at his job, thus denying the solace that identification with one's job can afford; and the town of Sitka will cease to be his home when control over the territory is returned to the United States. He is "a man who feels he was born into the wrong world. A mistake has been made; he is not where he belongs" (282).

In this way, Meyer is also like Mendel Shpilman, the murdered shell of a man who is discovered in the same hotel as Landsman, for Mendel was also without a home. As the son of the Verbover rebbe, Mendel's home should have been firmly established by privilege, power, and the walls that enclose his family's compound on the island of Verbov. As the performer of miracles and the Tzaddik Ha-Dor, the potential messiah believed to be born once in every generation and who will reveal himself if that generation is worthy, Mendel's home should have been linked to the Jewish faith and the nation of Israel. As a champion chess player, Mendel's home should have been among the chess players who esteemed him and considered him the best. But Mendel does not feel at home in any of these places and decides to seek a new home by rejecting his old one and setting off to find a place where he belongs.

Paradoxically, both Meyer and Mendel find their home in the very state of being homeless. And this is where faith is brought to bear, for as Meyer comes to realize, a "Messiah who actually arrives is no good to anybody" (349). "A hope fulfilled," we are told, "is already half a disappointment" (249) because once something hoped for is solidly before us, it can never live up to what we had imagined it would be. But a messiah who is always promised, and yet never arrives, allows us to continue in a state of faith and longing, imagining how good his arrival will be and even creating different scenarios of how our lives will change. This anticipation requires faith because faith is the certain belief in things we cannot see. If the messiah had arrived, we would no longer need to imagine what he or his arrival would be like because we would already know. Furthermore, an obvious messiah, a Tzaddik Ha-Dor who does all the right things and lives in all the right ways, would require no faith at all because he would be tangible and fully present. And Mendel is no obvious messiah. Although he shows initial promise, he fails horribly as the Tzaddik Ha-Dor. He is a heroin addict, he is gay, and he shames his father by running away on the night of his wedding. As Alter Litvak puts it, "Really, he was not much in the way of a Tzaddik Ha-Dor at all" (337). But at the same time that the waste of his life and its ignominious end in murder seems to emphatically underscore the fact that he is not the messiah, these things also make Mendel the kind of messiah that it takes faith to believe in. It takes a big imagination to see a heroin junkie as the Tzaddik Ha-Dor.

Part of the reason it is so hard to pin down whether or not Mendel really is the Tzaddik Ha-Dor is because he does, in fact, perform small and yet powerful miracles over the course of his short life. For example, after learning from Litvak at the beginning of their investigation that the murder victim is a Verbover Jew, Meyer and Berko go to Verbov Island to talk with Itzik Zimbalist, the boundary maven. As the boundary maven, it is Zimbalist's job to help the Verbovers get around the law prohibiting carrying things outside the home on the Sabbath by constructing real and imaginary walls out of string around the island. After a lifetime of circumventing the law, Zimbalist is a man who has long since given up on faith. Yet Zimbalist reveals to Meyer and Berko that when his mistress was dying of cancer in the hospital, Mendel had told him to say hello to her for him and to give her his blessing. Zimbalist did this and the next day his mistress mysteriously made a full recovery from the cancer that only the night before was on the verge of ending her life. The narrator relates that the "apparent miracle of the cancer cure forever altered his relations with Mendel Shpilman. . . . The boundary maven's faith in faithlessness had been shaken by a simple question—*How is she?*—by a dozen words of blessing, by a simple bishop move that seemed to imply a chess beyond the chess that Zimbalist knew" (124–25). This small, private miracle shatters the boundary maven because it happened without any hope or faith on his part. Furthermore, it was a miracle given to him, an adulterer—a man who should not by rights be given any blessing at all, much less the restoration of his mistress. In blessing the faithless adulterer, Mendel doesn't appear the way a "proper" messiah should. But again, a proper messiah is no messiah at all. Instead, Mendel performs profound miracles, in simple and quiet ways, for those who least deserve them.

This paradox or conflict between how Mendel appears on the surface and how people expect a messiah to be is underlined for Meyer and Berko when Zimbalist identifies Mendel's corpse in the Polaroid they show him:

"That's right," Zimbalist says at last. "Mendel Shpilman. The only son. He had a twin brother who was born dead. Later, that was interpreted as a sign."

Landsman says, "A sign of what? That he would be a prodigy? That he would turn out to be a junkie living in a cheap Untershtat flop?"

"Not that," says Zimbalist. "That nobody imagined."
(118–19)

Landsman is right—Mendel was both a chess prodigy and a junkie, things that no one on Verbov Island could have imagined from their Tzaddik Ha-Dor. But strangely, when he frustrates the early signs that lead the Verbovers to expect that he is the Tzaddik Ha-Dor, done most dramatically by irrevocably and publicly shaming his father in refusing to be married, Mendel seems to prove that he is indeed the Tzaddik Ha-Dor, a messiah who refuses to come.

The boundary maven, who befriended the young Mendel and arranged illicit games of chess for him, really should be an expert of faith and imagination already, so it is somewhat of a surprise to learn that he, too, was confounded by Mendel and his miracles. Since Jewish law forbids carrying anything outside the home on the Shabbat, Zimbalist's job is to draw homes and houses in the air by literally stringing together telephone poles and walls, fences and cliffs. As Zimbalist pours over his maps of the island, he can see walls that don't exist and imagine telephone poles as doorposts, strings as lintels. These new additions to Verbover homes can be conjured and drawn up anywhere to allow the Verbovers to carry money in their pockets or walk their dogs on the Sabbath, but they always remain rather delicate and ephemeral. For example, when "some idiot at Municipal put up a handball wall, right smack in the middle of a make-believe doorway between two light poles" (112), Zimbalist is called on to plot out "a workaround that will hold through sundown tomorrow, a salient in the great imaginary wall of the eruv" (113). Obviously, the people who work at the city couldn't see any walls standing in the way of their handball court because there weren't any walls there, only some string tied between the two light poles at the top. If they didn't look up, they would never even have seen the string. Nevertheless, the handball court, a structure that actually has a real wall, shatters the illusion and requires the boundary maven to see the great imaginary wall in a new way. He can then plot the points that must be tied by his crew, and the ephemeral wall can stand again until some other real structure plows through it. As the narrator explains, it is Zimbalist who must "guard the integrity of the make-believe walls" (110).

The narrator's initial description of Zimbalist's shop is an exuberant homage to the humble string:

> String, twine, rope, cord, tape, filament, lanyard, hawser, and cable; polypropylene, hemp, rubber, rubberized copper, Kevlar, steel, silk, flax, braided velvet. The boundary maven has vast stretches of the Talmud by heart. Topography, geography, geodesy, geometry, trigonometry, they're a reflex, like sighting along the barrel of a gun. But the boundary maven lives and dies by the quality of his string. (108)

Zimbalist must imagine all of Verbov Island not as a geography with clear demarcations between indoors and outdoors, households and market place, but as one big potential home in which can be contained all Verbovers with work to do on Shabbat. But his tools are not mystical and otherworldly. He uses string. Yet the simple strings, like Mendel's simple blessings, nevertheless produce miraculous transformations of the space of the island, tying together all the people who live there.

As he follows the threads of the stories about Mendel and the ways he transformed the people whose lives he touched, Meyer, the washed-up, alcoholic, homeless detective, comes to experience some of the paradoxical faith in which Mendel trades. While Meyer is most certainly a man without faith, he comes to believe in Mendel—or at least to see in the strung-out, wasted hull of a man the possibility of the messiah. When Bina and Meyer question the boundary maven for the last time, Zimbalist remarks that it is almost impossible to use the word *innocent* to describe men. "My whole life," he says, "I knew only one man I would use that word to describe" (388). Meyer's response is telling: "'Me, too,' says Landsman, missing Mendel Shpilman as if they had been, for many years, the best of friends" (388). Meyer's response reveals that although he is a man who is also cut free of almost all the cords that bind him to life, he has come to see in Mendel the possibility of what it would have been like to have known him or loved him or to have been blessed by him. That is to say, Meyer exhibits a kind of nascent faith, a faith that allows him to imagine what could have happened if the two had met. Meyer's belief in Mendel eventually becomes real enough that he doesn't just imagine what might have happened if they had met but feels sure that if they had met a miracle would have happened. The narrator explains that "for days Landsman has been thinking that he missed his chance with Mendel Shpilman, that in their exile at the Hotel Zamenhof, without even realizing, he blew his one shot at something like redemption" (410–11). Meyer can't regret missing a chance if he didn't believe in the chance in the first place.

Still, in keeping with the paradoxical nature of faith and the Tzaddik Ha-Dor, the messiah who never arrives, it is enough that Meyer regrets having missed Mendel. His regret is caused by the belief that if he *had* met Mendel, then he would surely have been blessed. And this is all that is required. The novel seems to suggest that one doesn't need to see Mendel himself to receive his blessing. Rather, Mendel's blessing is much more simple and much more profound than that. Mendel's father explains to Meyer and Berko that

> "there was something *in* Mendele. There was a fire. This is a cold, dark place, Detectives. A gray, wet place. Mendele gave off light and warmth. You wanted to stand close to him. To warm your hands, to melt the ice on your beard. To banish the darkness for a minute or two. But then when you left Mendele, you *stayed* warm, and it seemed like there was a little more light, maybe one candle's worth, in the world. And that was when you realized the fire was inside of you all the time. And that was the miracle. Just that." (141)

This is the same fire that Litvak will realize is "amoral, unconnected to goodness or wickedness, power or usefulness or strength" (352). But while Litvak mistakes the unconnected quality of Mendel's fire to mean that he can easily manipulate it for his political purposes, it is rather the fluidness of Mendel's fire that means he can generously pour it out on all he encounters, Jew or Gentile, rich or poor, faithful or faithless.

In the same way that Mendel is able to pass his blessing to Zimbalist in order for Zimbalist to pour it into the ear of his unconscious mistress and then give it to all the people in the hospital who presumably do not know Mendel, Meyer hears the blessing of Mendel without having met him and finds his life transformed. As Meyer tries to figure out the meaning of the chess game being played in the room where Mendel died and realizes the significance of the Vicks inhaler at b8, Meyer receives his blessing:

> Landsman feels it then. A hand laid on his, two degrees warmer than normal. A quickening, an unfurling like a banner in his thoughts. Before and after. The touch of Mendel Shpilman, moist, electric, conveying some kind of strange blessing on Landsman. (399)

Mendel's blessing unravels the problem of the chess game and reveals to Meyer the identity of the murderer. As the case wraps up, we find Meyer and Bina at the start of a tentative new relationship. And while Meyer had worried that he had missed his chance with Mendel, he realizes that "there is no Messiah of Sitka," because the messiah is, of course, the one who never arrives (411). And if the messiah never arrives, then he also can never be missed.

At the heart of the question of whether or not Mendel is the Tzaddik Ha-Dor is a desire for home or homeland. According to the Verbovers, if Mendel is the messiah, then he will help them return home to Israel and reestablish a Jewish Nation. But not all Jews living in Sitka are sure that Israel is where they belong or a place to which they want to come home. Meyer, for example, asks Berko if he really believes that there is a messiah who will take the Jews to Palestine. Berko answers with an uninterested shrug. Meyer himself realizes almost to his own surprise that Sitka is more of a homeland to him than Israel. He tells Cashdollar, the mysterious American agent who represents U.S. interests in the plot involving Mendel, "I don't care what is written. I don't care what supposedly got promised. . . . My homeland is in my hat. It's in my ex-wife's tote bag" (368).

Chabon reveals in an essay titled "Imaginary Homelands" that he has shared Meyer's struggles as well. In the essay,

Chabon explains that Israel is the core of the Jewish religion and thus, because he is Jewish, Israel is supposed to be his home both spiritually and physically. However, Chabon writes that although "certain venerable texts have long been interpreted as indicating not only that the land belongs to me by right but also that more than I want or am capable of wanting anything else in the world, I should want to live there . . . I remain unpersuaded by these arguments" (172). Indeed, the first time Chabon *did* visit Israel, he reports that "God knows I didn't feel I had come home" (174).

At the same time Chabon wonders if he is a man born into the wrong religious world, he also finds himself not at home in the world of "serious" fiction. Winning the Pulitzer surely confers a certain luster to an author, but Chabon writes that he was not at home in that world either because his great literary love remains genre fiction—detective stories, mysteries, hero stories, horror, and especially science fiction. In other words, Chabon, like Meyer and Mendel, is homeless, a man without a home.

But Chabon, like Meyer, seems to find a blessing in the story of Mendel Shpilman. Chabon's desire for both a spiritual and a literary home are redeemed or recovered in *The Yiddish Policemen's Union*. Chabon explains that

> for a long time now I've been busy, in my life and in my work, with a pair of ongoing, over arching investigations: into my heritage—rights and privileges, duties and burdens—as a Jew and as a teller of Jewish stories; and into my heritage as a lover of genre fiction. In all those years . . . I failed to notice what now seems clear, namely that there was really only one investigation all along. One search, with a sole objective: a home, a world to call my own. (170)

The speculative possibilities opened up by the genre of science fiction in *The Yiddish Policemen's Union* not only weave together to form the plot that drives the story of religious identity in the novel, but writing out these possibilities is also the very act of Chabon's homecoming. By writing an alternative history for the Jews, one that imagines what would have happened had the Roosevelt administration's 1938 proposal for making Alaska a "haven for Jewish refugees from Germany and other areas in Europe where the Jews are subjected to oppressive restrictions" been adopted, and imagining a place where the Yiddish speaker would feel at home, Chabon claims genre fiction as his literary home as well.

The novel thus suggests that finding a world to call one's own requires quite a bit of imagination and quite a bit of paradoxical faith. In order to have a messiah that never arrives, in order for "but there is no Messiah of Sitka" to become an affirmation of faith instead of a rejection of it, one must participate in the blessing of the messiah by finding this humble, mysterious faith. If you think about the messiah this way, as opposed to the certain and triumphant political messiah that the Verbovers and the U.S. government want Mendel to be, the Tzaddik Ha-Dor is not so much a person as a sacrament, something to be practiced by those who want to believe. A sacrament, such as communion or the Passover lamb, is something that is and is not simultaneously. Communion is the body and blood of Christ and it is not the body and blood of Christ. To be a sacrament, it must be both. This is the kind of paradoxical thinking at which Mendel himself was so adept. Zimbalist had explained to Meyer and Berko that "even as a kid, Mendel Shpilman seemed to intuit the messy human flow that both powered the Law and required its elaborate system of drains and sluices":

> "Fear, doubt, lust, dishonesty, broken vows, murder and love, uncertainty about the intentions of God and men,

little Mendel saw all of that not only in the Aramaic abstract but when it appeared in his father's study, clothed in the dark serge and juicy mother tongue of everyday life. If conflicts ever arose in the boy's mind, doubts about the relevance of the Law that he was learning in the Verbover court at the feet of a bunch of king-size ganefs and crooks, they never showed. Not when he was a kid who believed, and not when the day came that he turned his back on it all. He had the kind of mind that could hold and consider contradictory propositions without losing its balance." (121)

The blessing of the messiah, then, resides in being able to hold the contradictory idea that the messiah has arrived and that the messiah can never arrive, that Mendel Shpilman really is the Tzaddik Ha-Dor and that there is no Messiah of Sitka, and not to become unbalanced. The novel suggests that the regret Meyer feels because he thinks he has missed his chance with Mendel when they were both unmoored at the hotel together means that he has not missed Mendel at all. Meyer never met Mendel, but as it turns out, he didn't need to. The fire was inside of him all the time.

At the end, *The Yiddish Policemen's Union* suggests that faith and the ability to see the miracle is always entirely tenuous, hanging by a thread. But that tenuousness is the very feature that allows faith to be real and for there to be a little more light in the world. As Batsheva Shpilman, Mendel's mother, comes to understand, there is always a shortfall between what God intends and what ends up happening, and "they called that shortfall 'the world.' Only when Messiah came would the breach be closed, all separations, distinctions, and distances collapsed. Until then, thanks be unto His Name, sparks, bright sparks, might leap across the gap, as between electric poles. And we must be grateful for their momentary light" (214).

Discussion Questions about the Novel

1. What is faith? How does living with the certainty of things not seen work itself out in everyday life? Will that kind of faith always be unsettling to some degree or is it possible to find a point of balance?

2. Chabon often seems to equate faith with imagination. Are they the same? Does faith require imagination? Is it more than imagination?

3. Was Mendel Shpilman really the Tzaddik-ha Dor? Were the Verbovers right to venerate him when he was young, or did that pressure push him into a life of dissolution and drug addiction?

4. The collapse of Meyer's life seems to be rooted in his decision to abort Django and the doctor's subsequent report that nothing appeared to be wrong with the baby. Why is this experience so central to the novel and to Meyer's life? Was Meyer's initial decision a good one? Is it possible to recover from such an experience?

5. The genre of science fiction has been defined as the "fiction of setting"—that is, as a kind of fiction in which the setting drives the story more than the characters or the plot. Chabon insists that *The Yiddish Policemen's Union* is science fiction, and it has won several prestigious science fiction awards. Given that the novel is set in Alaska and speculates about what would have happened if Sitka had been a Jewish safe haven, do you think *The Yiddish Policemen's Union* is correctly categorized as science fiction? Why or why not? If the novel were set in some other place would the story be the same?

6. What does the narrator mean when he or she says that the boundary maven's "faith in faithlessness had been shaken by a simple question—*How is she?*"?

7. When Mendel's parents discuss why Mendel may have fled from his marriage, his father says that "a Tzaddik Ha-Dor is always hidden. That's a mark of his nature. Maybe I should explain that to him. Tell him that these—feelings— he experiences and struggles against are, in a way, the proof of his fitness to rule" (220). This comment makes it sound as if Heskel Shpilman *does* understand the paradoxical faith required to see Mendel as the Tzaddik Ha-Dor. And yet Heskel still acts as if Mendel has failed completely. What do you think Heskel meant by his comment to Batsheva?

▮ Other Books to Consider

—Michael Chabon, *The Amazing Adventures of Kavalier and Clay*. New York: Random House, 2000.

Chabon's magnum opus about the lives of Jewish artist Joe Kavalier and Jewish writer Sam Clay before, during, and after World War II. It tracks the story of how Kavalier and Clay became major figures in the nascent comic book industry in America. This book won Chabon the Pulitzer in 2001.

—Michael Chabon, *Maps and Legends: Readings and Writings Along the Borderlands*. San Francisco: McSweeny's Books, 2008.

This collection of essays written by Chabon over several years provides helpful insight into Chabon's works of fiction. It is also a great read in and of itself.

—Raymond Chandler, *The Big Sleep*. New York: A. A. Knopf, 1939.

> The first of the Philip Marlowe stories. A dying millionaire hires Marlowe to find out who is blackmailing his rebellious daughter and to make them stop.

—Nathan Englander, *The Ministry of Special Cases*. New York: Alfred A. Knopf, 2007.

> In 1976 Buenos Aires, Kaddish Poznan, an Orthodox Jew, makes his living by defacing the gravestones of Jewish prostitutes so their well-do-children can hide their pasts. When Kaddish's own son disappears and is "erased," Kaddish and his wife descend into a hellish world of bureaucracy to try to bring him back.

—Dashiell Hammett, *The Maltese Falcon*. New York: A.A. Knopf, 1930.

> This story introduces the original hard-boiled detective, Sam Spade. When Spade is hired to find a missing woman, his partner is shot and Spade is framed for the crime. As he tries to clear his name, Spade discovers a number of ruthless characters all hunting for an ancient gold statue of a falcon.

—Philip Roth, *The Plot Against America*. Boston: Houghton Mifflin, 2004.

> Roth's speculative alternative history asks what would have happened if Charles A. Lindbergh had defeated Franklin Roosevelt for the presidency in 1940. When Lindbergh accuses the British and the Jews of trying to force America into a foreign war, young Philip and his family must weather the wave of anti-Semitic hysteria that sweeps through the country.

Integrative Discussion Questions for Part Two

1. In *Purple Hibiscus*, Kambili both fears and longs for home. In *The Yiddish Policemen's Union*, the characters' actions center around their responses to home and homeland. Likewise, in *The Known World* many characters wonder what it means to be home or where they can find a place to belong: when Mildred and Augustus tell the young Henry that they will come back to Robbins's plantation to take him home, Henry cannot make sense of the word *home,* because his home on the plantation is the only home he knows. What is a home? Is it the place where you were born? The place you are most familiar? Is home the people with which you are with?

2. Chimamanda Ngozi Adichie, Edward P. Jones, and Michael Chabon all tell stories that have, at their roots, pain and suffering. In each of these cases, some characters respond through anger, and that motivation establishes the narrative action. How do these authors identify the sources of personal pain? Do they suggest that anger is an appropriate response? Do you, as a reader, come to feel that anger may, at times, be an appropriate response—and that characters are right to act upon that anger?

3. Think of the protagonists of *Purple Hibiscus, The Known World,* and *The Yiddish Policemen's Union.* What ideals do they hold? How are these ideals compromised, given the circumstances in which they find themselves? How do we evaluate these characters, given their compromises? Are there times when such compromising of ideals should be honored? Are there times when such compromising should be scorned? How do we make decisions between those responses?

4. Pain is individual, but our response to it may well be affected by the community in which we find ourselves—community defined as family, or as peer group, or as neighborhood, or as town, or as country. Think of the communities in which the characters of *Purple Hibiscus, The Known World,* and *The Yiddish Policemen's Union* live. How does the presence of those characters within their communities affect the ways in which they respond to pain and suffering? How should a community affect the ways in which we respond to pain and suffering?

PART THREE

"The Fateful Lightning"

"The Fateful Lightning"

I n Umberto Eco's *The Name of the Rose* (1980), Brother
William of Baskerville is faced with a terrible choice: he may
tell the truth and so be tormented by the Inquisition, or he
may be silent and allow the Inquisition to act with cruelty and injustice. He has been here before, chosen and faced the torment; he
has no desire to do so again. But the choice comes in the presence
of young Adso, his scribe and, more importantly, his disciple. In
the face of unbearable suffering, fear, and pain, William makes,
once again, the right choice—reluctantly, fearfully, hesitatingly,
he nonetheless makes the right choice. And that is enough.

Like fateful lightning in the darkness, our choices illuminate
who we are in the midst of a suffering world. And some of the
most powerful characters in fiction are like such fateful lightning,
illuminating as their ideals merge with their characters, and as
they remain true to themselves and their ideals—they can do no
less—and so shine brightly in a darkened world. They are Atticus
Finch, Tom Joad, Jean Valjean, Dorothea Brooke, Portia, Huck,
Hester Prynne, Trollope's Warden, and a thousand others whose
ideals are so much a part of their character that they seem one
thing. They act out of a sure and settled integrity. They act out
of themselves.

The characters of *Blindness, The Translator,* and *Gilead* all
find their ideals merged into their characters through the crucible
of their spiritual experience—though they define that spirituality in very different ways. The protagonists are drawn into real
suffering, and their characters prove to be neither brittle nor stub-
bornly unyielding; instead, their ideals lie within, indeed are a
part of their spiritual strength, so that it is impossible to think of

Sammar apart from her Muslim belief, or John Ames apart from his Protestant heritage, or the doctor and his wife apart from a religious tradition that may lie in tatters, but whose vestiges still inform.

How do we hold to our ideals in a pained world? these writers ask. Through the strength of the spiritual tradition out of which we come and by which we are strengthened into bolts of fateful lightning that illuminate the darkness.

BLINDNESS José Saramago
(1995)

On an ordinary day in a nameless city in an unknown
country, a man is suddenly struck blind while sitting at a
traffic light. The man who helps him home, the optometrist
who examines him, everyone in the doctor's waiting room
also become victims of this strange milky white blindness.
The group—the first blind man, the blind man's wife, the
doctor, the girl with dark glasses, the man with the eye
patch, the boy with the squint—along with the doctor's
wife, who feigns blindness in order to remain with her
husband, are quarantined by the government in an abandoned mental hospital. Although the initial group attempts
to impose some sort of order in this unstable situation, as
more and more victims begin to fill the asylum, the situation
becomes worse and worse. Food supplies are erratic and
finally cease altogether, while a band of armed thugs take
over and issue increasingly appalling commands. Finally the
situation comes to a head: one of the thugs is killed, there
is a fire, and the inmates are freed from the asylum and discover themselves lost in a society that is every bit as hellish
as the one from which they have escaped, for blindness now
afflicts everyone.

Guided by the doctor's wife, who for some inexplicable
reason remains able to see, the group enters the city and
learns of the complete breakdown of society. People are
reduced to wandering the streets, searching for food and
taking shelter wherever they happen to find themselves.
The streets are strewn with litter, abandoned vehicles, dead

bodies, and filth. The doctor's wife leads the group to her own home, where they are able to recuperate somewhat. The bonds between them are strengthened, and new relationships are forged as they discover their need for one another. In this new situation, they begin to make plans to leave the city to attempt to live in the country, but the plague ends as inexplicitly as it began, and the blind see once again.

On the Author

Born in the small, rural town of Ribatejo, Portugal, José de Sousa Saramago (b. 1922) was forced to abandon his formal studies at age twelve in favor of a trade school because of his family's difficult financial circumstances. He worked in a variety of manual labor jobs until the late 1950s, when he began to work for a publishing house. Although he published his first novel in 1947, he worked primarily as a journalist and translator until the success of his novel *Baltasar and Blimunda* in 1982 allowed him to devote himself exclusively to writing. Never one to shy away from controversy, in 1991 Saramago, a self-proclaimed atheist, published *The Gospel According to Jesus Christ,* a novel that was banned by the Portuguese government. In 1998 he became the first writer in Portuguese to receive the Nobel Prize. A longtime member of the communist party, Saramago enjoys using his literary fame to spread his political ideas.

Considering the Novel

In a time of crisis, in the midst of a disaster, where does the world turn for aid, for comfort? Those of faith can reply, along with the psalmist, that our help comes from the Lord, who made the heavens and the earth (Psalm 121:1–2), but for José Saramago, an avowed atheist, the answer is not so forthcoming. *Blindness,* then, can be seen as a working out of possible answers to that question. The original Portuguese title of the novel, *Ensaio sobre a cegueira,* hints at what the author is doing. The word *ensaio* means "essay," but it also implies experiment. So this fictional novel can also be regarded as a strange, horrific experiment. Saramago starts with the "what if" question and then structures his experiment: What if everyone in the world suddenly went blind? How would we react? How would people cope? Where would we turn for help? What would we learn about ourselves, our neighbors, our institutions, our government? Saramago explores where these questions will lead. He creates a generic city, populates it with nameless characters, and then infects them with a plague of white blindness. By depriving his subjects of sight, by submitting them to deep trauma, he hopes to uncover the true nature of humankind, because "perhaps only in a world of the blind will things be what they truly are" (126).

The characters in the novel are not the only ones challenged to make sense of a world in which they are suddenly blind. Readers, too, may feel that they have been dipped into a milky sea as they struggle to follow Saramago's sometimes dense prose. His largely unmarked dialogue makes it difficult to identify the speakers, and like the blind characters, the frustrated reader must sometimes guess from the tone or the content of a speech who is talking. But readers who persevere, who allow the prose to wash over them, will be rewarded with a tale at times grim and disturbing, but always absorbing.

Ironically, the opening lines of *Blindness* describe a world of light and color: the amber and red of a traffic light, the green man of a pedestrian signal, and the black and white of a crosswalk. The chatty voice of the narrator describes a typical urban landscape on a typical day; mundane musings about traffic jams and mechanical failures are interrupted by the cry of a stricken driver:

"I am blind." The driver has been plunged into a milky white sea for no apparent reason, and although the narrator maintains the same chatty tone, the novel shifts far from ordinary life into the extraordinary circumstance of a plague of blindness.

The novel is not interested in asking why this plague is happening; it is far more concerned with exploring how individuals and institutions react. What truths might be revealed? It seems that the first answer to that question, according to Saramago, is that people are basically evil and that life is hell. Systematically, all of the elements that make up modern life are examined and shown to be just superficial barriers against a hellish existence.

The first, and perhaps easiest, target of Saramago's savage attack is the government. When finally convinced of the reality of the plague of blindness, or "the white evil" as it is soon called, the government reacts with textbook incompetence. Officials carefully consider the economic, legal, and security implications of the possible locations for quarantine, but never for a moment reflect on the costs or benefits of their plan for the blind victims themselves. The newly blind meekly obey the officials who round them up and herd them into the asylum. Unfortunately, although the government moves with "speed and efficiency" (41) to isolate the plague victims, it rapidly proves itself to be uniformly inept. Bureaucracy and inefficiency reign, cloaked in high-sounding but empty rhetoric. The government's response to the crisis is simply to isolate the blind and the contaminated "until further notice":

> These very words, Until further notice, apparently deliberate, but, in fact, enigmatic since he could not think of any others, were pronounced by the Minister, who later clarified his thinking, I meant that this could as easily mean forty days as forty weeks, or forty months, or forty years, the important thing is that they should stay in quarantine. (38)

The government promises the quarantined that it will look after them, providing them with all that they need, declaring that "the Government regrets having been forced to exercise with all urgency what it considers to be its rightful duty, to protect the population by all possible means in this present crisis" (42). It presents the quarantine as an "act of solidarity with the rest of the nation's community" (43) and then issues a long list of instructions that makes it clear that the blind are to be abandoned to their own fate. They are threatened with death if they attempt to leave the building, warned that firemen will not intervene in case of fire, and instructed that they "cannot count on any outside intervention should there be any outbreaks of illnesses, nor in the event of any disorder or aggression" (43).

The soldiers who are assigned the task of carrying out the decrees reflect the government they serve. The supplies they bring are woefully inadequate. They abrogate any responsibility for the safety and well-being of the inmates once they feel that they themselves are safe from the "white evil." They are trigger-happy and so terrified of the inmates and the plague they carry that at the slightest provocation they empty their guns into the crowds of sightless inmates. Then, to absolve themselves, they declare, "The army regrets having been forced to repress with weapons a seditious movement. . . . We were not to blame, we were not to blame" (84). If the plague of blindness reveals "how things truly are," the government stands condemned. Ironically, even in the face of such obvious incompetence, the radio reports that "a rumour was going around that the formation of a government of unity and national salvation was imminent" (130). A crumbling society continues to seek deliverance from a corrupt and incompetent institution that promises "salvation."

As blindness exposes government corruption, it also exposes individual ugliness. Many of the victims of the plague of blindness reveal their worst qualities: their meanness, their pettiness, or their simple lack of consideration for their fellow victims once the veneer of civilization has been stripped away along with their sight. The plague magnifies small flaws, exacerbates tensions, and heightens sensitivity to slights. The first blind man's relief on being helped to his home is almost immediately replaced by doubt and suspicion. His mistrust is rewarded when the Good Samaritan, feeling slighted by the first blind man's lack of gratitude, proceeds to steal his car. (This same Good Samaritan later uses his own blindness as an excuse to grope another blind woman.) When both of these men are in the asylum, equally blind, they refuse to recognize the futility of their arguments and instead nurse old grudges until the doctor finally rebukes them, saying, "If your idea is to turn this place into a hell, then you're going about it in the right way" (47).

Life in the abandoned mental asylum where the blind victims are quarantined goes from bad to worse. At first the situation seems merely grim, since the blind victims cannot be troubled by the dinginess or peeling paint of the facility. The first six internees are only given enough food for five people, and the meals come without glasses, plates, or cutlery. These are minor inconveniences compared with the problems to come. As more and more victims of the plague arrive at the mental hospital, the government's list of fifteen instructions is faithfully repeated unchanged each day, but the promised food and supplies becoming increasingly erratic and insufficient. Soon all two hundred and forty beds are filled and new inmates are forced to sleep on the floor. Hunger and distrust lead to squabbling. Overcrowded facilities mean a lack of privacy and overtaxed plumbing. The clean milky whiteness of the blind people's world contrasts with the increasingly fetid environment in the asylum. The asylum soon becomes a filthy, stinking hell.

The latrines are overflowing, the floors become slippery with excrement, and

> no imagination, however fertile and creative in making comparisons, images and metaphors, could aptly describe the filth here. It is not just the state to which the lavatories were soon reduced, fetid caverns such as the gutters in hell full of condemned souls must be, but also the lack of respect shown by some of the inmates or the sudden urgency of others that turned the corridors and other passageways into latrines, at first only occasionally but now as a matter of habit. (131–32)

What is perhaps most horrifying is how quickly the inmates learn to adjust to each new level of loss and squalor. Each time conditions worsen, the internees adjust and recalibrate their expectations of civilized life. The lack of privacy, the petty squabbling, the stench of unwashed bodies all become "normal."

And things get worse. The last group of internees to arrive takes control of the food supplies and demands that the other blind people turn over their valuables if they wish to eat. Using the threat of a handgun, and with the assistance of a man who was blind from birth, this small group of thugs threaten and intimidate the others into giving up the few material possessions they still possess if they wish to eat. As they are waiting to turn over their belongings to the thugs, the doctor comments, "I cannot imagine anything worse than our present existence" (144). But once again the blind internees adjust and rationalize even this situation. "If things continue like this, we'll end up once more reaching the conclusion that even in the worst misfortunes it is possible to find enough good to be able to bear the aforesaid misfortunes with patience" (151). They have not, however, yet encountered the worst misfortunes.

"After a week, the blind hoodlums sent a message saying that they wanted women. Just like that, Bring us women" (166). The internees protest, they are appalled, they refuse, but in the end, because they have to eat, they acquiesce. The thugs reign; might and violence appear to triumph over weakness and decency. Savagery is unleashed, and the reader is subjected to harrowing scenes of mass rape. Saramago has put the world to the test and seems to have proven that human nature is essentially evil. But throughout this profoundly disturbing, tragic, and sometimes simply disgusting vision, there are still elements of goodness, rays of hope.

Although the plague of blindness has shown humanity's dark and evil nature, there are some whose basic kindness, nobility, and compassion have been brought into focus and strengthened by adversity. Like the other victims, the doctor experiences fear and even despair when he realizes that he has gone blind, but unlike them, he summons up courage and continues to think primarily of others instead of himself. His foremost thoughts are of his wife and of the public at large. In spite of his own fear and worry, he takes time to alert the authorities to the possibility of a larger problem.

The girl with the dark glasses is identified first as a party girl, then as a prostitute, and finally as a whore, but her actions in her self-assigned role as surrogate mother to the young boy with the squint show that she is willing to think about others before herself. The man with the eye patch has already established his good character in the doctor's waiting room before he goes blind, not complaining when the first blind man jumps to the head of the line and is examined before those who were already waiting. His kindly and gentle nature is further revealed and magnified once he becomes blind. He remains patient in the face of adversity and later defends the actions of the doctor's wife when she kills the leader of the thugs.

But the person whose basic goodness becomes most apparent is the doctor's wife. As soon as she realizes that her husband will be quarantined, she makes plans to be with him and to help him, going so far as to feign blindness herself in order to remain with him. It is her directions, her organizational skills, that keep the situation in the first ward from deteriorating into total chaos. She makes an improvised rope from strips of blanket so that the blind will not become lost. She devises ways for the blind to identify their beds. She serves as spokesperson to the guards outside the asylum.

Although the doctor's wife is the only person who does not go blind, her eyesight is not the source of her strength and wisdom. Indeed, what some might consider a great blessing is for her a burden, even a curse: while the others can only imagine the horror of their physical surroundings, the doctor's wife is forced to see the depths to which they have sunk, to witness their progressive degradation. At times she even wishes she, too, were blind (58). But fortunately, she has vision, both literally and figuratively. When the thugs hijack the food supply and demand payment before distributing meals, the doctor's wife has the first inklings of a plan. She holds back and hides a pair of scissors, thinking that "an ordinary gun does not make much noise. A pair of scissors even less" (155). But when, during the first horrific night of mass rape, she is presented with an opportunity, her traditional conception of right and wrong is too strong. "I can kill him, she thought. She could not" (181). The evening ends with the death of one of the women, an event that strengthens the resolve of the doctor's wife. A few nights later she slips into the room where the women are being raped and uses the scissors to kill the leader of the band of thugs, in the process rescuing the woman being raped by him at that very moment. But even then the nightmare does not end.

The food supplies are cut off, the blind people begin to starve, and the complaints begin. It is then that the influence of the doctor's wife is seen most clearly. The novel suggests that merely being in the presence of a strong moral force may have a positive moral effect on others. When confronted by a person of courage, compassion, and vision, some of the internees overcome their fears and prejudices and are inspired to "do the right thing." The old man with the eye patch volunteers to head an offense against the remaining thugs barricaded in their ward. Joining the group is the girl with the dark glasses, whom the ordeal of the gang rape has transformed: "Women are born again in one another, the respectable are reborn as whores, whores are reborn as respectable women, said the girl with dark glasses" (204). The woman rescued by the doctor's wife also signs on and, after the initial attack is unsuccessful, it is she who devises the plan that ultimately brings an end to the long nightmare of their imprisonment. She sets fire to the barricade protecting the thugs, killing herself in the process and burning down the asylum.

As they huddle together for warmth in the cleansing rain that follows the fire, the group of seven recognizes that the only way to survive is as a group, supporting one another in community. The novel could end here, leaving the blind people—having learned a lesson about the importance of depending one another—to begin a new life outside the asylum. But the novel goes on. It is as if the horror of the asylum were not sufficient, or not sufficiently extensive. As the group ventures out into the city, they discover that the hell of the asylum was merely a miniature version of the hell developing outside its walls.

The last third of the book examines the fate of the wider civilization outside the asylum. While the atrocities endured by the blind internees might be explained away as aberrations due to the intensity of a closed, trapped community, the outside world has no such excuse. As the former inmates venture out, they are horrified to learn that the rest of the world has suffered the same or a worse fate. Every one of the institutions in which humans put their trust has failed. The former internees have already learned of the failure of the government and military. Soon they realize that the basic infrastructure, always taken for granted, has also stopped working. There is no transportation, no piped water, no electricity, no true homes. In a matter of weeks, society has been reduced to a nomadic, hunter-scavenger civilization where "someone who was blind and had left their home would only manage to find it again by some miracle" (222). Dogs hunt in packs, but people form only loose associations, as the blind become separated and unable to find one another again.

Once again, the trajectory of the situation goes from bad to worse. The initial shock of discovery of the loss of civilization becomes compounded as the group explores the world outside the asylum more thoroughly. The accumulation of horrific details parallels the situation in the asylum earlier: the streets are full of excrement, dead bodies are scavenged by packs of wild dogs, people are constantly hungry and reduced to eating whatever they can find—even killing and eating raw meat. The physical suffering is accompanied by an existential angst. Crowds surround wild-eyed street preachers who alternately proclaim the gospel of supernatural or rational systems (298, 310).

As in all times of crisis, people turn to the Church. Just as other institutions have been found lacking, so too, Saramago shows the Church as irrelevant in this crisis. When the doctor and his wife enter a church, they find it crowded with blind people seeking solace, but they also discover that someone has vandalized all of the religious images there. Each of the images, including the crucified Jesus, has been "blinded" with either paint or bandages. They theorize "that a priest must have committed the worst sacrilege of all times and all religions, the fairest and most radically human, coming here to declare that, ultimately, God does not deserve to see" (318). Those within the church panic when they learn of the blind images. For them "it was tantamount to having told them that they were surrounded by the living dead" (319). The novel depicts this as a scene of horror, an abomination, and an indictment of religion as yet another failed element of society. Viewed through unbelieving eyes, a blind Christ is simply a testament to the ultimate abandonment of the world to its own devices. Yet for a believer, the image of a blindfolded Christ in this world of blind people is extremely powerful and deeply comforting. Not only has God been made flesh and come to dwell among us, he has truly shared in our weakness. Instead of being viewed as a weakened or powerless God, the blindfolded Christ is a sign of "God with us." Here the novel seems to have escaped from the grasp of its author to proffer a different, even opposing interpretation.

As in the first part of the novel, the reader is not left without hope. Here it comes in the form of a mystical "dog of tears" who befriends the doctor's wife, providing her with comfort and companionship. And, as in the asylum, not everyone has descended quite so far into the depth of incivility. The group, led by the doctor's wife, makes its way to the first blind man's flat, where they discover a blind writer who has been assiduously keeping a record of what has happened. Remembering all the squabbles and disagreements, the petty arguments and the grudges that seem to be as epidemic as the plague of blindness, it is with some surprise that we see the first blind man and his wife come to an amicable agreement and easily give up their claim to their flat. Perhaps it is through contact with the doctor's wife or simply the influence of living harmoniously, if under difficult circumstances, that causes them to acquiesce and behave so genteelly.

Indeed, all of the members of the group have grown in compassion and empathy for one another. Being blind, they become conscious that they cannot depend on outside systems for help; but as lone individuals, they are also helpless. Their profound need for cooperation and mutual support is clear to them, and they realize that the only way to survive is to put their faith and trust in other individuals.

Although Saramago rejects Christianity, he does employ deeply religious imagery when he wants to show fellowship, love, and hope. Saramago might be called a Catholic-inflected author, even though he declares himself an atheist, because he seems unable to escape the influence of growing up in a Catholic country. When the group of seven pilgrims finally reaches the doctor's flat, a home away from the filth and squalor of the streets, they celebrate with a ceremony very like the Eucharist. The doctor's wife

> put [the water] on the table, went to fetch the glasses, the best they had, of finest crystal, then slowly, as if she were performing a rite, she filled them. At last she said, Let's drink. The blind hands groped and found the glasses, they raised them, trembling. Let's drink, the doctor's wife said again. In the middle of the table, the lamp was like a sun surrounded by shining stars. When they had put the glasses back on the table, the girl with the dark glasses and the old man with the eyepatch were crying. (278)

There is a sacrament of baptism, as well, on the night of their arrival to the doctor's flat. The group has arrived at a safe place and is ready to begin a new life as blind people in this strange world. But first they must slough off the old and the memories of all that happened in the asylum. The skies open and the rain pours down and the three women go out naked to the balcony to let the rain wash away the filth that has accumulated during their ordeal. They are cleansed and transformed and ready to begin a new life as part of this small community. Even though Saramago wants to posit a thoroughly humanistic solution to the problems of his blind society, images of a community of faith continue to creep in.

The ending of the novel is abrupt, unexpected. Just as swiftly as the plague of blindness began, it suddenly ends. One by one the blind people regain their sight. Just as there was no reason for the epidemic to begin, there is no explanation of why it is ending. But now, for the first time, the victims question, why did we become blind? And the reader, too, wonders why? What was the purpose of this strange experiment? One of the characters has an answer: "I don't think that we did go blind, I think we are blind, Blind but seeing, Blind people who can see but do not see" (326). The reader remembers the exhortation with which the novel began, "If you can see, look. If you can look, observe."

Discussion Questions about the Novel

1. The blind inmates learn to adjust to each new level of degradation in the asylum much in the way Jews adapted to the increasingly restrictive and degrading decrees of the Nazis during the Holocaust. Does this show a remarkable adaptability and resilience or a depressing acquiescence and submission to evil?

2. What is the function of the proverbs in the novel? Do they contribute to your understanding of the situation? How do they affect the tone of the novel as a whole?

3. Why is the blindness white? What might that choice suggest about Saramago's sense of the human condition?

4. The doctor's wife is the moral center of the novel, and she is also the only one who does not go blind. Is her ability to see a "reward" for her goodness? Or is it easier for her to be good because she can see?

5. At the end of the novel, presumably all the blind people will regain their sight. Why has the plague ended? What lessons, if any, have been learned?

Other Books to Consider

—Geraldine Brooks, *Year of Wonders*. New York: Penguin Books, 2001.

When plague attacks a seventeenth-century English village, the pastor urges the villagers to think of the broader community and isolate themselves. The novel follows a young widow as, in this isolated context, she struggles to retain her humanity in the face of bigotry, fear, and suspicion.

—Albert Camus, *The Plague*. Translated by Stuart Gilbert. New York: Alfred A. Knopf, 1948.

An Algerian city is infected by the plague and subsequently quarantined. The isolation affects internees differently, causing them to ponder issues of love, duty, and morality.

—P.D. James, *The Children of Men*. New York: Alfred A. Knopf, 1992.

No children have been born in the world for twenty-five years. People must decide how they will live, what is of value, and where they can find hope, given the fact that humanity seems to be coming to its end.

—C.S. Lewis, *Perelandra*. London: The Bodley Head, 1943.

In the second book of Lewis's Space Trilogy, a perfect world is invaded by evil and Ransom must decide if it is morally acceptable to kill in order to protect goodness.

THE
TRANSLATOR   Leila Aboulela
(1999)

Sammar, a young widow born in London but raised in the
Sudan, is working as a translator for Rae Isles, a professor of
Islamic Studies at a university in Aberdeen, Scotland. Four
years ago, following the death of her husband, Tarig, in an
automobile accident, Sammar returned home to Khartoum, to
the house of her mother-in-law and aunt, Mahasen. But when
Sammar wishes to remarry an older widower with two wives,
attracted by his kindness and his devotion to Islam, she and
Mahasen quarrel. Sammar leaves her young son, Amir, with
her aunt and returns to Aberdeen, shaken and bereft.

   After an accidental visit to Rae's flat in the company of
her friend Yasmin, Sammar and Rae deepen their relationship, meeting in the Winter Gardens, eating lunch together,
and talking on the telephone. Despite Rae's deep respect for
Islam, he considers himself an agnostic, much to Sammar's
distress. When it becomes apparent that he is unable or unwilling to become a Muslim, Sammar returns to Khartoum
and reestablishes a relationship with her family and her
country, despite her growing love for Rae.

Leila Aboulela (b. 1964) grew up in Khartoum, Sudan,
where she attended university and was awarded a degree
in economics. Her mother, who was born in Egypt, was a
university professor and the first female demographer of the
Sudan, and her grandmother studied medicine in the 1940s.
Aboulela earned a master's degree in statistics from the

London School of Economics and later lived for several years in Aberdeen before moving to Abu Dhabi. It was during her student years in Great Britain that she began to express her Islamic faith more publicly and to wear the hijab. She has said in an interview that she felt free to choose religion, and that it provides her more stability than any national identity: "I can carry [religion] with me wherever I go, whereas the other things can easily be taken away from me."

The Translator is her first novel. She won the Caine Prize for African Writing for her collection of short stories, *Coloured Lights* (2001), and has also written a second novel, *Minaret* (2002).

Considering the Novel

"Reader, I married him."

These are the words that begin the final chapter in Charlotte Brontë's novel *Jane Eyre,* and they perfectly encapsulate the story of the young governess who falls in love with Rochester, her older, mysterious, world-weary employer. The shape of *Jane Eyre*'s plot is familiar to anyone who has ever read—or lived through—a romance. Younger woman meets more experienced man; they fall in love but hesitate to declare their passion; problems and misunderstandings, including those imposed by friends, family, and differing social classes, ensue and drive them apart; illness often intervenes; when all seems hopeless, the lovers are reunited and, dear reader, they marry.

In *The Translator,* Leila Aboulela follows this well-known plot trajectory. Her Jane Eyre is Sammar, a Sudanese widow living in Aberdeen, Scotland, who falls in love with her employer, Rae Isles, a professor at the university whose specialty is Islamic Studies. Sammar is younger than Rae, less experienced in the world—his portfolio includes not just academic honors, but a rebellious past, drugs, and two ex-wives—and, as his Arabic translator and a university staff person, she occupies a lower social position. Since Sammar is a devout Muslim and Rae is an agnostic, and since devout Muslim women neither casually date nor marry outside their religion, any sexual frisson between the two seems doomed from the start. In other words, what we have here are all the necessary ingredients for a classic romance novel.

Aboulela's skill as a novelist, then, lies not in the construction of her plot, which covers a well-known and even well-worn terrain, but rather in the ways she shapes her characters into people that we as readers wish to know better. Sammar is not just a young woman, but a widow and a mother. Although her experience of the world may not be as varied as that of Rae, she is not a naive innocent. The depth of her grief, her inability to function as a mother after her husband is killed in an automobile crash, and the daily challenges of living as an immigrant in a foreign culture have left her barely more than a survivor. But she is a survivor who clings to a deep faith and a job she does well. The kaleidoscopic juxtapositions of these roles—widow, immigrant, mother, Muslim, translator—as they alternately clash and resolve into patterns both muted and vivid are what bring the novel to life.

Many of the most poignant moments of the book occur when Sammar contemplates the loss of her husband. She thinks of her grief as diamond shaped, "its four angles stapled on to her forehead, each shoulder, the top of her stomach. . . . The diamond shape of grief made sense to her: her forehead—that was where it hurt when she cried, that space behind her eyes; her shoulders—because they curled to carry her heart. And the angle at the top of her stomach—that was where the pain was" (4). This evocation of grief is beautifully portrayed, but it is also searingly etched into Sammar's body. She feels languid and lost, unable even to prepare a simple meal or to purchase furniture for her apartment.

Although this grief began with the death of her husband, it is not, she recognizes, tied simply to his loss. Or, at least, it does not stem entirely from the fact that he, as a husband, is no longer present.

For Sammar, widowhood means not just that she has lost Tarig; she is honest enough to recognize that their marriage had migrated from passion into affection. More distressingly, she has also lost her emotional home with his mother, Mahasen, and his sister, Hanan. Since childhood she has been bound more deeply to them than to her own father, mother, and brother, Waleed. Indeed, she remembers how she shrugged off her own family, making herself a gift, "a child to be moulded" (7). Because she has known Tarig since childhood, been promised to him almost from birth, to lose him is literally to lose part of herself. Looking at the tidy walkways in the Winter Gardens as she talks with Rae, she remembers the casual games she played with Tarig and wonders, "Was it Tarig who always shaped designs in the dust? Or was it [me]?" (27). Little wonder that in losing him—and his family—she has lost herself. And she is doubly bereft because in losing her husband—and his family—she has also been exiled from her beloved Sudan. Contemplating her life in Scotland, she realizes that "she had lived four years as if home had been taken away from her in the same way Tarig had" (33).

The Sudan and Scotland, or more precisely Khartoum and Aberdeen, figure almost as strongly as characters in the novel. Khartoum, the city of two rivers where "something old and whole was in the air" (50), looms large both in Sammar's memory and later in reality when she returns home. It is all "heat, dryness, desert dust" (136), and her family are eager to turn on the sporadic air-conditioning and leave the heat behind. But the dryness doesn't desiccate Sammar. Instead, she realizes that "her bones were content with that, supple again, young. They had forgotten how they used to be clenched" (136).

Clenching is a good term to describe Sammar's experience of Scotland. Aberdeen itself is a "small, compact city," crowded with pavements, billboards, and traffic lights, nearly always too wet or too cold for a woman raised in the desert. Thinking about the difference in climate, Sammar muses that "she had learnt early on, from the first year she had come with Tarig, that the winter sun of this city was colder than its winter rains. Many times before that lesson was learnt, she had seen the bright sun from the window, felt its warmth through the glass and gone out lightly dressed, only to shiver with incomprehension and suffer as every inadequately dressed African suffers in the alien British cold" (65). Because Sammar has learned to clench her body against the alien cold, the warmth she feels when she sits on a park bench beside Rae in the Winter Gardens immediately turns her mind toward home.

And yet she is so disconcerted by the unexpected conjunction of cold Scotland and the heated Sudan, that she can only describe it as a fit or hallucination. She goes home from the gardens feeling ill, and when she wakes up "feeling radiant, light, she thought she must have had something like an epileptic fit" (6). Coming out of Rae's flat after her visit there with Yasmin, she feels that she has "stepped into a hallucination in which the world had swung around. Home had come here" (20). Later, after talking with Rae on the telephone, she revisits the hallucination: "Home and the past had come here and balanced just for her" (41). Indeed, what both Sammar and Rae experience as "home" is located more in the geographies of the heart than of the landscape. "You make me feel safe," Rae tells Sammar, and she thinks gratefully that "nothing she said startled him" (39), an unexpected treasure for an immigrant accustomed to stares, puzzled glances, and well-meant, but awkward, toleration.

The depth of Sammar's displacement—both emotionally and geographically—is shown most keenly in her inability to mother

Tarig's child. And that is the way she primarily sees Amir, as a figure who triangulates between her dead husband and her mother-in-law. Why couldn't he have died, she thinks shortly after Tarig's accident. A child is replaceable; a husband is not. Although she feels guilty at the thought (79), it is not until she returns to Khartoum and severs her ties with Scotland that her heart begins to find again its center of gravity and to settle on her small son. Although he has already begun school, Sammar creates a game in which she carries him about, the two of them pretending that he is once again a baby in the cold, faraway land of Scotland.

Yet amid all the displacements of Sammar's life, one constant remains—her identity as a Muslim. Although there are beliefs to which she as a Muslim subscribes, the heart of her faith is practice, primarily the practice of prayer. The gray monotony of her days, the passivity into which she has let herself sink, the "dreamy heaviness" (67) that is Scotland, is relieved only by the five daily times of prayer. She experiences them as "the only challenge, the last touch with normality, without them she would have fallen, lost awareness of the shift of day into night" (16). In much the same way as she needed physically to re-bond with Amir, Sammar physically enacts her faith, finding in the ritualized body postures and formulaic words the nourishment that slowly pushes her back to life: "Her prayer mat had tassels on the edges, a velvety feel, a smell that she liked. . . . When she finished praying she sat for the *tasbeeh*, her thumb counting on each segment of her fingers, three for each finger, fifteen for a hand" (37). More than wife to Tarig, more than mother to Amir, more than daughter to the looming parental figure of Mahasen, more even than lover of Rae, Sammar finds her primary identity in being Muslim. And at the heart of being Muslim is the notion not of sacrifice but of surrender. *Islam* literally means "submission to the will of Allah," and throughout the novel Sammar is engaged in a battle to subdue her grief, her disconnectedness from her son, her homesickness, and finally, her love for Rae.

Sammar embraces surrender to the will of Allah as necessary for the good life. In contrast to the Western regulation of civil behavior, with its explicit "signs and polite rules" (4) about where to walk your dog and how to behave in public, Sammar revels in the deep guidelines Islam provides for her life. Considering, for instance, the rules that governed the period of mourning after Tarig's death, Shammar "thought of how Allah's sharia was kinder and more balanced than the rules people set up for themselves" because they allowed her to grieve for "four months and ten days . . . a specifically laid out time, not too short and not too long" (69). When she is tempted to think of her dismal life in Aberdeen as the result of an impersonal fate, she catches herself up short: "'No,' she reminded herself, 'that is not the real truth. My fate is etched out by Allah Almighty, if and who I will marry, what I eat, the work I find, my health, the day I will die are as He alone wants them to be.' To think otherwise was to slip down, to feel the world narrowing, dreary and tight" (73). And later she affirms that "nothing that Allah forbids His servants is good. It will only diminish them, ultimately or soon, in this life or the next" (116). Where a non-Muslim might find the obligation to pray, the fast of Ramadan, the prohibition on cross-gender relationships, and other Islamic duties to be restrictive, for Shammar, the "narrowing, dreary, and tight" perspective is the one that excludes Allah. When she considers that Rae might not merely be a non-Muslim but actually a nonbeliever, an atheist, she is nearly as distraught as when she realizes she will not be able to marry him.

It might seem that Sammar's role as a translator would make her a natural emissary between Rae, the man she loves, and Islam, the faith she loves. But Sammar consistently feels that she has failed to bring her two loves together or to speak appropriately to Rae about Islam. A translator by definition is a person who lives between—*trans*—two worlds, two cultures, two languages. But everything about Sammar resists such oscillating movement. Although she has traveled around the world and even holds a British passport—much to the envy of her Sudanese relatives— she longs only to return to Khartoum.

Just as the Qur'an cannot be translated but must be experienced in its pure, original Arabic, so, too, for Sammar translation is always conversion, and conversion is a nonreplicable, personal experience. As a child, she translated herself from her birth family to Tarig's family. As an adult, she refused to translate herself into Scottish culture, instead letting herself become "numb over the years" (70) while her heart remained in the Sudan. She cannot translate Islam for Rae, try as she may; it is he who must be translated into a Muslim, reciting the *shahadah* not merely as a rote formula but as a means of bearing witness to a transformed life. When she sits down to reply to Fareed's formal letter proposing marriage with Rae, Sammar realizes that "she was going to write two letters in two languages. They would say the same thing but not be a translation" (190), for a translation could not express the truth of what she needed to say in each letter. And when Sammar asks Rae why he was unable to say *shahadah* in Aberdeen after he said he loved her, he can only reply, "In the Qur'an it says that pure women are for pure men . . . and I wasn't clean enough for you then" (196–97). Rae recognizes his need to be translated into, and to bear witness to, Islam for himself.

The ending of this novel may pose difficulties for the North American reader. The difference in social class and professional rank between Sammar and Rae raises questions about the propriety of their relationship. Is it appropriate for an employer, given his status and power, to pursue a liaison with an employee?

Perhaps somewhat belatedly, Sammar raises this very issue when she asks Rae, "What did you *imagine* all this was going to lead to?" (128). Despite Rae's immersion in Islamic culture, he fundamentally misreads both the strength of Sammar's commitment to her faith and her expectations of him.

Might it also seem too "pat" for Rae to convert to Islam after Sammar has given up all hope of their romance and vowed to pray for his conversion simply for his own good? Is their reunion, as a reward for good behavior, simply too gratuitous? Possibly. But Aboulela has set her romance novel within the structure and the strictures of the Islamic faith, and as Sammar notes, almost in passing, "She envied Fareed because he was married and she was not, and marriage was half of their faith" (108). Although the notion of marriage as essential to religious faith may be difficult for North American readers to accept, the very casualness with which Aboulela makes this statement reveals its foundational nature in at least some branches of Islam. Furthermore, the surrender motif of part 2 of the novel—from Sammar's decision to leave Scotland and later to resign from her job, to her acceptance of the harsh life in Khartoum, to her willingness to pray unselfishly for Rae's conversion—is critical to Sammar's maturation as a Muslim. Living in Khartoum, she recognizes "deprivation and abundance, side by side like a miracle. Surrender to them both" (161). And from such surrender comes release, awareness, vividness, the reawakening both to life and to the dreams that lighten and purify the soul.

In its depictions of faithful Muslims, the novel itself is a gentle critique of modern Western society. Early in the story, when Sammar meets Rae in the Winter Gardens, she notes that "he seemed to understand, not in a modern, deliberately non-judgmental way but as if he was about to say, 'This has happened to me too'" (6). The difference between tolerance, with its abstract sense of equality and justice, and the empathy that values deeply rooted, embodied experiences could not be more clearly drawn. Despite her ability to function as a modern, working woman, Sammar is not at home in the modern world. There is an element of nostalgia, of course, to her desire to return to Khartoum, to forego the air-conditioning and sit on the roof absorbing the desert air. But there is also a deeper sense in which she recognizes that she—and perhaps Waleed and Rae and Yasmin and even Aunt Mahasen—only *function* in the modern world, as moving cogs in the grand capitalist machine. They don't truly live. Which is why even when she desires Rae's conversion so that she can marry him, she also longs for him to be truly whole. Her friend Yasmin takes a different and modern view of the matter: it would be professional suicide for Rae to convert to Islam, because, as she explains to Sammar, "No one will take him seriously after that. What would he be? Another ex-hippy gone off to join some weird cult. Worse than a weird cult, the religion of terrorists and fanatics" (21). Aunt Mahasen, too, prizes modernity. "An educated girl like you, you know English . . . you don't need marriage," she tells Sammar at the beginning of their great quarrel (13), particularly marriage to a religious man. But for Sammar, life without Allah is no life at all. When she realizes that Rae may be an atheist (a position he quickly denies), she recognizes that "never in her life had anyone she cared about been an unbeliever. Not religious, yes, not praying, not particularly caring about what's right or wrong, but always the faith was there, always Allah was there. His existence never denied. It was unbearable to think that Rae was so unaware" (94).

Unbearable. For Sammar many things seem unbearable: the death of Tarig; alienation from Aunt Mahasen; exile from Khartoum; dreary Aberdeen winters; the loss of Rae's love. In the end, though, only loss of faith—or its absence—is truly unbearable. Which is why Sammar is able to transmute her love for Rae into prayers for him and is able to create a meaningful life in Khartoum without him.

And yet *The Translator* is a romance novel with the obligatory happy ending. It is not as terse as Jane Eyre's "Reader, I married him." Instead, Aboulela ends with a dream sequence. A Muslim marriage requires only two witnesses and the giving of gifts. The dream outlines the gifts the bride and groom exchange—cloths of silk, wool, and cotton and a bowl of musky, milky liquid—all reminiscent of the dreams and conversations they have already shared. And the two witnesses? Those, dear readers, are we.

Discussion Questions about the Novel

1. Some North American readers may find it easier to empathize with Aunt Mahasen, who tells Sammar not to marry again so quickly, than with Sammar herself, who seems to come to life only as a wife or a wife-in-waiting. To what extent do you think Aboulela is simply working out the traditional romance plot and to what extent do you think she may be providing a window into a legitimate life choice for Muslim women?

2. Although Shammar often prays in the university mosque and later at the mosque in Khartoum, and she reflects that when she prays with others "her heart [is] held steady by those who had faith like her" (74), we see relatively few scenes of communal religious life. Even when she is comforted by the women from the Aberdeen mosque after Tarig's death, she is barely able to acknowledge their presence and kindness (8–9). Is Sammar's isolation necessary to her character? Is

it necessary to the plot, which focuses on the developing relationship between herself and Rae?

3. One of the recurring images Aboulela uses is that of froth. Sammar's grief, her inability to mother Amir, her passivity, all are described as dirty froth, like that which rises to the surface of the water when you boil chicken (6–7). Again, when Sammar leaves Aberdeen and Rae, she looks out her airplane window and sees "the pale frothy sea" (132). Do you find this an effective symbol of Sammar's inner life?

4. Although politics are not central to the novel, Sammar and Rae do discuss world situations and the roles to be played by contemporary Muslims. Recognizing that the novel was published prior to 2001, how does Aboulela help you better understand the varieties of Islam and the roles played by terrorist organizations in the Muslim world?

Other Books to Consider

—Leila Aboulela, *Minaret*. New York: Black Cat, 2002.

> A privileged young Muslim woman from Sudan is forced to adapt to the harsh life of a London immigrant when her father is arrested and killed by his political enemies. Indifferent to her faith before the catastrophe, she becomes a faithful adherent of Islam, despite the difficulties of working as a servant and cherishing a forbidden love.

—Monica Ali, *Brick Lane*. New York: Scribner, 2003.

> Nanzeen, a Bangladeshi immigrant to Britain, moves through her East London neighborhood and arranged marriage with deceptive calm until she encounters the possibilities of enlarging—and defying—her racial, religious, and personal constraints.

—Charlotte Brontë, *Jane Eyre*. London: Smith, Elder and Company, 1847.

A classic tale of forbidden and triumphant love that crosses barriers of age, social class, insanity, bigamy, and experience.

—Mohja Kafh, *The Girl in the Tangerine Scarf*. New York: Carroll & Graf, 2006.

The coming-of-age story of an American Muslim girl, this novel moves from an immigrant upbringing in Cincinnati, to flirtations with Islamic fundamentalism during student years, to a mature faith as a young professional.

GILEAD Marilynne Robinson
(2004)

Synopsis

In 1956, knowing that he is soon to die, the seventy-seven-year-old Reverend John Ames begins a long letter addressed to his young son. The letter will be compensation for the conversations they will never have, the father-son experiences they will never share. In it John Ames hopes not only to narrate family memories, but also to explain why he chose to spend most of his life as a Congregational minister in the small Iowa town of Gilead, and to pass along his faith to his son. As he recounts his life, and that of his grandfather, parents, brother, wives, and friends, he discovers that he is writing as much to himself as to his son, and he explores what it means to practice patience, humility, and faithfulness as a Christian and as a pastor. Midway through the novel, the return to Gilead of his namesake, Jack Broughton, stirs up fears for his small family and causes the Reverend Ames to examine his own life and his vocation as a minister.

Written as a set of intertwined memories and short narratives, *Gilead* stretches from the Civil War to the beginnings of the civil rights movement as it considers, from the perspective of a small midwestern town, a century of American life.

On the Author

Marilynne Robinson (b. 1943) is the author of *Housekeeping* (1980), winner of the Hemingway Foundation/PEN Award for a first novel; *Mother Country: Britain, The Welfare State and Nuclear Pollution* (1989), a nonfiction account of the nuclear power industry in England; and numerous essays, including those collected in *The Death of Adam* (1998). *Gilead* won the Pulitzer Prize in 2005. Her newest novel, *Home* (2008), focuses on the Boughton family during the same years portrayed in *Gilead*. Robinson has said that *Gilead* allowed her to bring together her interests in theology and in the history of the Middle West.

She completed her undergraduate degree at Pembroke College and recieved a PhD in English from the University of Washington, where she specialized in Shakespeare studies. A professor at the University of Iowa Writers' Workshop, Robinson has helped shape the current generation of American writers.

Considering the Novel

Gilead opens with a quiet conversation about that most mysterious of human experiences: death. "I told you last night I might be gone sometime," the Reverend John Ames says to his son, "and you said, Where, and I said, To be with the Good Lord, and you said, Why, and I said, Because I'm old, and you said, I don't think you're old" (3).

But John Ames is old—nearly seventy-seven years old, in fact—and he has heart disease, and he is dying. On the other hand, as the questions suggest, his son is very young, the seven-year-old blessing of an unexpected and blessed marriage. From its opening lines, then, the novel sets itself a difficult task: to record in advance the conversations this father and son will never enjoy as adults, to pass down the family legacy in the form of a long letter. "Your mother told you I'm writing your begats," says the Reverend Ames, "and you seemed very pleased with the idea" (9).

John Ames begins his "begats" with memories of the old man who loomed over his own childhood. His grandfather, the first John Ames, was a fiery preacher-turned-abolitionist who moved from Maine to Kansas with the "Free Soilers" to prevent Kansas from declaring itself a slave state. A "wild-haired, one-eyed, scrawny old fellow with a crooked beard, like a paintbrush left to dry with lacquer in it" (81) and an acquaintance of John Brown, he was the "most unreposeful human being I ever knew," his grandson recalled (49). He and his contemporaries "were like the Hebrew prophets in some unwilling retirement, or like the primitive church still waiting to judge the angels. . . . They were bodacious old men, the lot of them" (50). They were also difficult to live with. Between his temper, his penchant for visions and violence, and his tendency to give anything and everything away, Grandfather Ames managed to exasperate his son and daughter-in-law, with whom he lived in his later years, and intrigue his grandson. John Ames's mother complained that "she could probably go to any town in the Middle West and see some pair of pants she'd patched walking by in the street" (31), and he himself recalled that after one of his visions "the old man would be radiant and purposeful and a little more flagrant in his larcenies" (97).

Grandfather's larger-than-life persona threatens to overshadow his son, the second John Ames, a Congregational minister in the small rural town of Gilead, Iowa. This John Ames is quiet, reserved, and most important, a pacifist. In a final confrontation with his aging father, he tells him, "I remember when you walked to the pulpit in that shot-up, bloody shirt with that pistol in your belt. And I had a thought as powerful and clear as any revelation. And it was, This has *nothing* to do with Jesus. Nothing. Nothing. And I was, and I am, as certain of that as anyone could ever be of any so-called vision" (84–85). Yet when Grandfather Ames disappears into Kansas shortly thereafter and fails to return, his son takes the twelve-year-old John Ames and sets out on a penitential odyssey to find his father's gravesite.

The awkward rhythm that rocks the relationships of the three John Ameses—father, son, and grandson—underlies a question

Robinson explores throughout the novel: how is it possible to pass down to one's progeny the gift of faith, understood as both holding faith in God and as holding to the contours of a faithful life?

For Grandfather Ames, a faithful life is marked by passion, visions, an aggressive restlessness that plucks injustice out by the roots. He might as easily shoot you as give you his last pair of pants. His son, in contrast, goes reluctantly into the army at the close of World War I and returns to "sit with the Quakers on the Sabbath" (87). Young John Ames inherits both genes: he has a passionate streak and a temper to match; he values his grandfather's "strenuousness in ethical matters" (90), but he chooses, like his father, to enact the faithful life in disciplined quietness. The danger of such a measured response is that it can seem mundane and inadequate. "My father," Ames remembers, "acted from faithfulness to the truth as he saw it. But something in the way he went about it made him disappointing from time to time, and not just to me" (7). Certainly disappointment marks the relationship between Ames's father and his older brother, Edward. Somewhat in awe of his son's intellectual gifts, John Ames and the entire congregation sacrifice to send Edward off to seminary and then to Germany to study with the best theological minds of the late nineteenth century only to have Edward return to Gilead an atheist. A quiet, well-mannered atheist, but an atheist nevertheless, his mind stocked with Ludwig Feuerbach's arguments against religion, although without the remnant of natural piety Feuerbach himself retained.

As the younger son, John Ames watches these conflicts from the distance of late childhood, absorbing and moderating his grandfather's passion, his father's passivity, his brother's intellect. His family bequeaths him other gifts as well—a midwestern taciturnity, a fine work ethic, modest ambitions, the capacity for patient, long-term relationships. Although intrigued by Edward's intellectual mentors, John Ames chooses to return from seminary to Gilead, to take up his father's pulpit and devote his life in ministry to his rural Iowa congregation. For nearly fifty years he works as an exemplary pastor among his small flock. He baptizes and buries and eats far more casseroles, pickles, and contrived salads than any sane man should. Paging through a popular magazine, he thinks, "There should be a law to prevent recipes for molded salad from appearing within twenty pages of any article having to do with religion" (145). He preaches over two thousand sermons, marries his childhood sweetheart, Louisa, and buries her along with their baby daughter, Angeline. It is these two losses that establish his lifelong habits of solitude and reflection. "I don't know why solitude would be a balm for loneliness," he says, "but that is how it always was for me" (18–19).

The young John Ames develops two great loves that sustain him in his solitude: his ministerial vocation and a love for the beauty of the world. In an early emblematic scene, he writes about a warm, perfect day when he and his playmates baptized a litter of young kittens down at the creek. The beauty of the sacrament and the beauty of sensual things merge together in a lovely and memorable tableau. "I still remember how those warm little brows felt under the palm of my hand," he tells his son. "Everyone has petted a cat, but to touch one like that, with the pure intention of blessing it, is a very different thing. . . . There is a reality in blessing. . . . It doesn't enhance sacredness, but it acknowledges it, and there is a power in that. . . . The sensation is of really knowing a creature, I mean really feeling its mysterious life and your own mysterious life at the same time" (23). And elsewhere, watching his second wife and son play with Soapy the cat, he simply murmurs, "Ah, this life, this world" (9). To see the miracle of the world—and to acknowledge it as miracle and receive it gratefully—mediates between his grandfather's restless passion and his father's tamped-down plainness.

John Ames first experiences his peculiar affinity for the miraculous world when he stands at his grandfather's grave, listening to his father's long prayer of penitence:

> I tried to keep my eyes closed, but after a while I had to look around a little. And this is something I remember very well. At first I thought I saw the sun setting in the east. . . . Then I realized that what I saw was a full moon rising just as the sun was going down. Each of them was standing on its edge, with the most wonderful light between them. It seemed as if you could touch it, as if there were palpable currents of light passing back and forth, or as if there were great taut skeins of light suspended between them. I wanted my father to see it, but I knew I'd have to startle him out of his prayer, and I wanted to do it the best way, so I took his hand and kissed it. And then I said, "Look at the moon." And he did. . . . My father said, "I would never have thought this place could be beautiful. I'm glad to know that." (14–15)

Although his father acknowledges the beauty of the moment, he discounts any talk of a miracle; the alignment of sun and moon is an unusual natural phenomenon, nothing more. But John Ames recognizes the something more, the blessing that graces his father's act of penance, "the glory that my grandfather had somehow emanated out of his parched repose" (48). He inherits, and transmutes, the faith of both his father and his grandfather.

And so he finds blessing, glory, miracle in performing the duties of his ministerial vocation, his "trade" as he calls it. He sits down to calculate the number of sermons he has written—"writing has always felt like praying" (19)—and discovers, somewhat to his surprise, that he has composed a shelf full of theological meditations, some 2,250 sermons in all, almost all of them, he tells his son, written "in the deepest hope and conviction. Sifting my thoughts and choosing my words. Trying to say what was true. And I'll tell you frankly, that was wonderful" (19).

The first half of the novel unspools in such muted vignettes and reflections, leavened with good fun. The inset story of the abolitionist townspeople who dug so many tunnels that they undermined their own main street includes the pitch-perfect image of an inebriated horse, snoring gently, his head propped on the lip of a six-foot deep hole. Robinson, in the voice of her protagonist, offers many smaller intact narratives as well. Sometimes a few short sentences draw the reader into an entire world of memory and shared experience, as when she describes the "weight of light—pressing the damp out of the grass and pressing the smell of sour old sap out of the boards on the porch floor and burdening even the trees a little as a late snow would do. It was the kind of light that rests on your shoulders the way a cat lies on your lap. So familiar" (51). At other times, humor is on the menu. Describing a three-casserole supper "with two kinds of fruit salad, with cake and pie for dessert," Reverend Ames decides that "my flock, who lambaste life's problems with food items of just this kind, had heard an alarm. There was even a bean salad, which to me looked distinctly Presbyterian, so anxiety had overspilled its denominational vessel" (127). The episodic format of these short narratives at times resembles a series of loosely connected meditations that the reader might savor in short, daily increments.

The novel gains narrative traction, however, with the arrival of John Ames Boughton, the son of the Reverend Ames's longtime friend, the Presbyterian minister Robert Boughton. Jack, as he is known, is not quite the serpent in the garden, but he is, and has been throughout his life, a disruptive force. As a baby, he was given as a namesake to the widowed John Ames, a compensation for the children he would never have. Jack grows up wild, thoughtless, and adored by his father and sisters, particularly Glory, who later returns home to care for her father. Temperamentally, Jack resembles Grandfather Ames more than any other character in the book, although he lacks the moral compass by which all generations of the Ames clan have steered. He is charming, aggressive, theologically astute, and footloose. And he is the same age as the Reverend John Ames's beloved wife, Lila.

The sexual jealousy, never overtly articulated but always thrummingly present, that now pulsates through John Ames's letter to his son, adds an edge of temptation, danger, and introspection to the memoir he is crafting. Jack's intrusion into the narrative reminds John Ames that he is old and dying. Jack also adds a larger, worldly dimension to the story, which had been settling into the domestic confines of the Ames household.

It is a domesticity the Reverend John Ames cherishes and that he had never expected to enjoy after the death of his first wife, a miracle that ends both his loneliness and his solitude. Above all, it is the wonder of this intact family, secure in its love, that he wishes to pass on to his young son:

> I'd never have believed I'd see a wife of mine doting on a child of mine. It still amazes me every time I think of it. I'm writing this in part to tell you that if you ever wonder what you've done in your life, and everyone does wonder sooner or later, you have been God's grace to me, a miracle, something more than a miracle, You may not remember me very well at all, and it may seem to you to be no great thing to have been the good child of an old man in a shabby little town you will no doubt leave behind. If only I had the words to tell you. (52)

It is his wife who has created this miracle. As readers, we never see her clearly. She is, John Ames tells us, beautiful, but we sense that hers is a beauty only he can truly see or describe. We do, however, hear her voice and the flat cadences that hint of her origins without revealing them: "It don't matter," she would say when she forgave someone, to which Ames added, "It was as if she were renouncing the world itself just in order to make nothing of some offense to her. Such a prodigal renunciation, that empty-handed prodigality I remember from the old days. I have nothing to give you, take and eat" (149). Her past is of no concern to her husband, or to the novel; only her clear-eyed acceptance of the present, her "earned innocence . . . stripped of all the accretions of smugness and pretense and triviality" (30).

Her entrance first into the church building on a "blessed, rainy Pentecost" (203), then into the fellowship of believers, and then into John Ames's life, is marked by fierce need. Her husband remembers her seriousness, "almost like a kind of anger. As though she might say, 'I came here from whatever unspeakable distance and from whatever unimaginable otherness just to oblige your prayers. Now say something with a little meaning in it'" (21). What she actually says, however, when she asks to be baptized is simply, "No one seen to it for me when I was a child. I been feeling the lack of it" (207). When John Ames looks at her and at their son, he sees the beauty of love and the beauty of the world merged, as fragile as the soap bubbles they blow for the cat one afternoon. Watching them, he reflects that they are "too intent on the cat to see the celestial consequences of [their] worldly endeavors" (9).

It is just such fragile beauty and celestial consequences that Jack's return to Gilead disrupts. Indeed, he threatens all three of John Ames's loves: his family, his ministerial vocation, his delight in the world. The threat to the family is the clearest and closest to his heart. Although Lila Ames is no naïve young maiden, she is, in a deep and pure way, a good person, and one acutely attuned to suffering. Insofar as Jack presents himself as a lost soul, a needy lamb, she is drawn to protect and shelter him. Insofar as he is John Ames's namesake, she is happy to welcome him into their home. Knowing the deceptiveness of Jack's charm and the casually cruel way he has treated women and children in the past, Ames longs to reveal his perfidy and thus protect his small family from harm.

But Jack also threatens John Ames's love of the world because his beautiful face and lighthearted friendliness is compounded, at least in Ames's eyes, of calculated self-interest. There is no miracle here—no alignment of sun and moon; no blessing; none of the simple beauty of a woman, a child, a cat, and soap bubbles on a sunny afternoon.

Most deeply, perhaps, Jack threatens John Ames's own sense of his ministerial vocation. It is a vocation that is not incidental to his own faith, which, though inherited, he has made his own through study, long practice, and deliberate choice. John Ames is a minister out of conviction, not habit. He has made a life out of his love for God and neighbor. But now that life is threatened by one of his most imminent neighbors—his own namesake—threatened not only because Jack has the power to disrupt both the Ames and Boughton households, but also because he forces John Ames to recognize the constrictions of his own heart. "Heathen that he is," he intuitively thinks when he looks at Jack (120).

These are not threats that are easily resolved. To turn Jack away is potentially to wound both Robert Boughton and his own small family, all of whom are inclined to welcome Jack as the returning prodigal son. Yet to allow Jack free access to his home is to encourage an intimacy that Jack, at least in times past, has consistently abused. More insidiously, to refuse to comfort or counsel Jack is to deny his own ministerial vocation. "I must be gracious," John Ames thinks. "My only role is to be gracious." But merely acting gracious is insufficient. "Clearly," he muses, "I must somehow contrive to *think* graciously, about him, also, since he makes such a point of seeing right through me" (123). But contriving is precisely the problem, for as Reverend Ames is well aware, his inability actually to love Jack, his tendency to see in his namesake only "sly unanswerable meanness" (190), exposes his own pride and self-righteousness, his "sullen old reptilian self" (167).

The difficulties are compounded when Jack reveals his own tale of displacement—his marriage to an African-American woman, the birth of their son, their separation due to prejudices from both blacks and whites. With the revelation that Jack, too, has suffered domestic injury and entered into his own abyss of loneliness, Robinson delicately brackets the life of the Reverend John Ames with the racial upheavals of the Civil War and the nascent civil rights movement. Faced with intractable social injustice, does the quiet life of a midwestern pastor matter?

The answer to that question partly comes in the theological discussions that crowd the last third of the novel. Reflecting on the Ten Commandments, on the lives of Abraham, Sarah, Isaac, Hagar, and Ishmael, on the mysteries of God's providence and election, the Reverend John Ames argues that no church, no pastor, no Christian is "sheltered and parochial," since all partake in the "universal and transcendent life" that bypasses neither small towns nor large cities, where "the bread is the bread and the cup is the cup everywhere, in all circumstances, and it is a time with the Lord in Gethsemane that comes for everyone" (114). The halting imperfections of those who search for truth "have no bearing at all on the Truth itself, which could never conceivably be in any sense dependent on me or on anyone," he reflects (172). But in addition to theological discourse, there is also the witness of ordinary lives lived out of conviction and out of awareness of the grace that burns "as a sort of ecstatic fire that takes things down to essentials" (197).

As John Ames struggles to pass his legacy of faith to his young son, he memorializes these essential things. There are limitations. He cannot mold his son in his own image; he cannot protect him from poverty and anxiety; he cannot guarantee that he will grow up to be a John Ames rather than a Jack Boughton. But he can tell the stories that have shaped his own life: The story of his grandfather's visions. The story of his father giving him half an ashy biscuit and his kneeling in the rain to eat it amid the ruins of the charred Baptist church (102). The story of his beautiful, serious wife, her brow wet with the water of baptism (93). The story of his nearly seven-year-old son, red-shirted and "standing up on the seat of your swing and sailing higher than you really ought to, with the bold planted stance of a sailor on a billowy sea" (111). The story of his forgiving Jack Boughton and recording "the beauty there is in him" (232).

In the end, John Ames can offer little but himself—husband, lover, father, preacher, prophet—and his blessing. And yet, that is a remarkable thing to consider.

Discussion Questions about the Novel

1. In the Hebrew Bible, Gilead is associated with an ointment or balm that heals wickedness. Is there a balm in this *Gilead*? What is the healing ointment? What are the problems it may cure?

2. A novel about "begats" calls to mind the first book of the Bible, Genesis, with its lists of genealogies that—in older translations—include the litany "and Abraham begat Isaac, and Isaac begat Jacob, and Jacob begat Joseph." What similarities exist between these biblical characters and the character of John Ames? Is he more like an Abraham—an

old man with a young son? Or more like an Isaac—a man of modest demeanor who stands between his fiery grandfather and the deceitful charm of his Jacob-like namesake, Jack? Does he himself resemble Jacob, who loved his younger sons more than his elder sons? Do such biblical allusions add to the richness of the novel?

3. In earlier eras, mothers often wrote "advice books" to their children, particularly when they knew they were about to die. In many ways, *Gilead* is an advice book written by a father to his son. How might the book be different if it were written by Lila? What kind of advice book would you write to your own children?

4. *Gilead* spans the period of American history from the Civil War to the nascent beginnings of the civil rights movement. Why do you think Robinson chose to set her story of ministers and the passing on (and loss of) faith in the 1950s? Does this time period suggest that John Ames's nonironic view of religious belief is part of the past, but would be difficult to sustain in the present?

5. The Protestant sacraments of baptism and the Lord's Supper are highlighted many times in this novel, from the young John Ames's baptism of the kittens through his eating of the sooty biscuit after the steeple fire (95, 102) to his giving communion to his young son (69–70). At one point he says, "I've always loved to baptize people, though I have sometimes wished there were more shimmer and splash involved in the way we go about it" (63). Why might Robinson refer to the sacraments so often? What dimensions do these references add to the passages in which they occur?

6. Robinson often writes in proverbial, gnomic sentences that seem like small set-pieces of beautiful prose. Do you find such sentences illuminating or do they slow down the story line? Do you find the style evocative or ponderous?

Other Books to Consider

—Georges Bernanos, *The Diary of a Country Priest*. Translated by Pamela Morris. New York: The MacMillan Company, 1937.

A young French priest comes to understand the life of his provincial parish, the darkness of his own heart, and the call to true humility.

—Willa Cather, *My Ántonia*. Boston: Houghton Mifflin, 1918.

A classic evocation of pioneer life. Narrated by the American-born Jim Burden as he recalls his friendship with the Bohemian immigrant girl, Ántonia Shimerda, the novel traces the possibilities and challenges the American West posed to its frontier families.

—John Fox. *The Trail of the Lonesome Pine*. New York: Scribner's Sons, 1908.

A romance western set in the Appalachian Mountains, the novel follows the feud between the Tolliver and the Falin clans, as well as the encroachment of the coal mining industry. In the 1936 movie version, the outsider John Hale, who falls in love with June Tolliver, is played by Fred MacMurray.

—Stephen B. Oates, *To Purge This Land with Blood: A Biography of John Brown*. Amherst: University of Massachusetts Press, 1984.

A detailed study of the life of John Brown, which examines his passions, his obsessions, his delusions, and his place in American history.

Integrative Discussion Questions
for Part Three

1. All novels participate in narrative formulas, which they may follow slavishly, or thwart, or play with. Leila Aboulela, for example, seems to begin with the conventional romance formula in *The Translator,* but then quickly complicates it. Consider *The Translator, Blindness,* and *Gilead* as participating in the formula of the love story. In what ways do each of these stories take up elements of a conventional love story and then complicate them?

2. Imagine a conversation in which Marilynne Robinson, José Saramago, and Leila Aboulela are speaking about the concept of salvation. How would each of these writers describe salvation? How would they expect a human being to achieve salvation—if, that is, they believed it to be possible?

3. Marilynne Robinson, José Saramago, and Leila Aboulela each write out of a strong religious tradition, whether that tradition is reflected in the novel's meaning, the novel's art, the novelist's imagery, the novelist's language, or the novelist's means of carrying narrative meaning. Not all readers, of course, will share in these religious traditions. How, then, does the writer help the reader first to understand the tradition and its power, and then to be moved, deepened, and broadened by an experience that is, essentially, other?

4. Saramago seems to picture humanity as being motivated almost entirely by brutal self-interest—and yet, there is the doctor's wife. Robinson shows an elder John Ames whose Christianity is deep and filled with righteous conviction—but

he wears guns up to the pulpit. And Aboulela gives us Rae, an Islamic scholar who has left all faith behind—but who comes back to it out of love. Where might each of these three writers find agreement as they describe human nature?

PART FOUR

"His Truth is Marching On"

"His Truth Is Marching On"

One of the last lines of the final quatrain of Julia Ward Howe's "Battle Hymn of the Republic" is an affirmation of a commitment to ideals, following a reference to Christ's birth "in the beauty of the lilies": "As he died to make men holy, let us die to make men free." The reference, of course, is to emancipation, since Howe was writing in 1862. The commitment is total: given this ideal, we strive for it to the death. In this, perhaps less committed, age, the line is regularly adapted to something less rigorous: "As he died to make men holy, let us live to make men free."

Three years later, Julia Ward Howe would see her ideal become reality—following the greatest human cataclysm the nation has ever seen. Sometimes ideals do enter the real world. Sometimes the magical happens. Sometimes goodness finds us.

Khaled Hosseini's *The Kite Runner*, Cormac McCarthy's *The Road*, and Kate DiCamillo's *The Tale of Despereaux* each look for a truth to be marching on—and each contains a character who is willing to push toward that truth with a commitment that goes beyond the self: "let us die to make men free." The father in *The Road* is committed not only to the survival of his beloved son, but also to the prevention of disillusionment in a world that seems utterly lost. Hosseini's Amir returns to his beloved Afghanistan to find it changed beyond recognition, but he returns to repay a debt of love and loyalty. And Despereaux, having escaped darkness once before, is willing to go down into it to rescue Princess Pea; it is his quest. Quest "is an extraordinary word, isn't it?" says the narrator of this novel. "So small and yet so full of wonder, so full of hope" (221).

The miracle here is that their quests are full of hope and wonder—for the other. The father, Amir, and Despereaux begin their quests knowing well that they may die to make an other free. And no matter how fearful or hopeless or cynical they may be, they act to fulfill those quests.

THE KITE RUNNER Khaled Hosseini
(2003)

Synopsis

Young Amir grows up in Kabul, Afghanistan, in the years immediately preceding the Soviet invasion. His is a world of both privilege and peril. Amir's father is fabulously wealthy, and Amir enjoys true friendship with Hassan, the son of his father's servant. But even within his happy home, Amir must come to terms with guilt, jealousy, and betrayal. The novel follows Amir's boyhood in Kabul, the new life he begins in America as a young man, and the trip he makes back to Afghanistan in 2001 to help old friends hurt both by the young Amir and by the cruel course of Afghani history.

On the Author

Khaled Hosseini (b. 1965) was born in Kabul, Afghanistan, the son of an Afghani diplomat and a high school teacher. As a boy, he developed a close friendship with a family servant, a man in his thirties who took an active interest in him and who eventually served as the model for Hassan in *The Kite Runner*. The family was living in Paris when the Soviet Union invaded Afghanistan, and they emigrated to the United States. Although Hosseini pursued a career in medicine and worked as a doctor for eight years, he now spends his time writing fiction. He began writing *The Kite Runner* in March 2001. Hosseini's second novel, *A Thousand Splendid Suns* (2007), also draws from his childhood memories of Afghanistan.

Considering the Novel

"Come. There is a way to be good again." Rahim Khan's words over the telephone (2, 192) do not actually tell Amir very much. They do not tell him that Hassan has been shot, or that Hassan has left behind a son named Sohrab, or that Sohrab has been sold to Assef. But they do tell readers a great deal about the sort of novel they are entering. For all their elusiveness, Rahim Khan's words are quite direct: they make no attempt to cloak basic morality—good and bad—under fancy language. They clearly acknowledge Amir's own sense of sin, and they name "good" for what it is. They accomplish this serious moral business, however, in a decidedly restrained and understated way. Rahim Khan does not say, "You need to get back to Kabul *now*! It's a matter of life and death!" There is no hysteria in his voice, no melodrama, no exclamation marks. Just nine short words, offered with moral purpose and simple elegance.

Much of the novel has this feel of an old folktale. It involves exotic settings and characters who are larger than life; its suspenseful plot is shaped with economy and precision; it develops a clear moral theme. In fact, however, *The Kite Runner* is a collection of tales, falling out into three major episodes, each of which follows a fairly traditional plot. The first, set in old Kabul, is a tragedy in which the protagonist knowingly betrays his friend and a happy family is torn and scattered. Episode two, in California, is a comedy, in which a young man discovers his calling and marries a beautiful young woman despite some initial conflict with her somewhat crusty father. Episode three, the return to Kabul, is a hero quest, deepened with sober tones of personal redemption.

Hosseini demonstrates a storyteller's knack for structure and pace. He knows, for instance, how to drop a significant hint to create suspense. When we hear Rahim Khan say that "there is a way to be good again," we wonder not only how Amir might regain his goodness, but how he lost it in the first place. Evocative lines such as this fill the early chapters of the novel: "But I never got to finish that sentence. Because suddenly Afghanistan changed forever" (34). Especially when they appear at the beginning or ending of a chapter, lines such as these create openings that a reader waits for the story to fill.

At the same time, Hosseini gives the story an astonishing degree of coherence and closure. Some of the tightest closure occurs between characters, as when Amir realizes that he is not reconciled with Baba and Hassan, but that in some ways he *is* Baba and Hassan. "Baba and I were more alike than I'd ever known," he muses, reflecting on the way that Baba had betrayed Ali. He goes on to recognize that "Rahim Khan had summoned me here to atone not just for my sins, but for Baba's too" (226). His identification with Hassan is even closer. Through most of *The Kite Runner,* a first-time reader assumes that the title refers to Hassan, because he is named as such on page two. Only on the last page do we discover that it also refers to Amir, who is running a kite for Sohrab and who has spent the entire novel becoming the kite runner.

Hosseini also builds closure by including several astonishing coincidences in the final third of the book. The childhood bully and the adult bully turn out to be the same person. Assef rapes Hassan; he seems also to have raped Sohrab. Hassan threatens to shoot Assef in the eye with a slingshot; Sohrab really does shoot him in the eye with a slingshot. Ali is infertile and adopts Hassan; Amir and Soraya are infertile and adopt Sohrab. When Amir encounters a beggar on the streets of Kabul who knew his mother, he acknowledges that the encounter is something that "most non-Afghans would have seen as an improbable coincidence," but he assures us that "in Afghanistan, and particularly in Kabul, such absurdity was commonplace" (251).

Whether this assurance can be extended to all of the symmetries described above is an open question for any reader, but such tidiness is to be expected in certain kinds of stories, such as a folktale. We accept that folktales will feel somewhat artificial. Their carefully crafted closure is a part of what makes them appealing—and perhaps even reassuring. We expect Sohrab to somehow find a home with Amir, and we are not disappointed. The story does not develop predictably, but it does develop with a certain inevitability.

It is not just the themes and plot of *The Kite Runner* that make it feel like a folktale, however. The setting and characters also contribute to that texture. Young Amir leads a charmed life. His Kabul is not quite the world of Ali Baba and the Forty Thieves, perhaps, but there is an Ali and a Baba; there is adventure and intrigue. In fact, Amir's entire childhood milieu has the feel of a fabled world. There is abundant and almost unexplained wealth. Baba seems to spend most of his time in the novel sitting with Rahim Khan and smoking cigarettes, but he lives in a splendid home, throws lavish parties, gives endless gifts. He and Amir might not have flying carpets, but their American-made vehicles—a mighty black Mustang for the father, a Schwinn Stingray for the son—serve as status symbols with mildly mythical auras. To the Afghanis in the story, Baba and Amir's life must have seemed exotically American; to modern Americans, it seems exotically Afghani. The story opens in a kind of ideal dream world that almost transcends time and place.

Appropriate to such a setting, many of the characters who surround Amir cast a legendary glow. There is Baba, the fearless wrestler of bears and challenger of armed Russian soldiers, whose very presence seems to animate and protect all those who are near him. There is Hassan, whose humility and loyalty to Amir are almost too profound to be human, and who runs kites by some mysterious inner instinct.

Despite these idealistic settings and characters, however, Amir's childhood is not really perfect; it is perfectly real. Amir himself has all of the uncertainty, insecurity, and petty jealousy of a human boy, and he faces situations similar to those faced by children in every part of the real world: the comfort of camaraderie, the thrill of competition, the pressure of family expectations, the threat of bullies.

What makes *The Kite Runner* such a success is the way it blends the fantasy and craftsmanship of classic tales with the mundane unpredictability of real life. Without its fantasy and craftsmanship, *The Kite Runner* would be nothing more than a curious human-interest story about an Afghani family. Without its realistic elements, it would be an entertaining and unbelievable dream, morally instructive perhaps, but no more believable than *One Thousand and One Nights*.

Yet *The Kite Runner* is characterized by a strong sense of disillusionment. In fact, the story is filled with instances of disappointment. Lying in his hospital bed with bandaged wrists, Sohrab is "tired of everything." When Amir asks him what he wants, Sohrab says plainly, "I want my old life back." Amir is at a loss for words. All he can say is "Oh, Sohrab" (354).

There is a strong dose of empathy in those two words, because Amir himself loses his old life several times throughout the novel. First and foremost is the kite tournament that he and Hassan win. Amir dreams of winning his father's approval by winning the contest, and he imagines in detail how his life will change: he and Baba will laugh together, travel to all kinds of exciting places, discuss the short stories Amir has been writing. And most important, Baba will forgive him for killing his mother (56). In a purely realistic story, a character would have to come to terms with the hard impossibility of this dream. Hosseini complicates things, however, by allowing the dream to come true. Amir and

Hassan win! But the world has changed, and the price of Amir's wish—which he himself calculates with cold precision (77)—is Hassan's rape. Following centuries of moral storytellers, Hosseini demonstrates the folly of human wishes not by denying them but by granting them, and by showing the ways in which the real world would erode our fondest dreams if they were made real.

This sense of disillusionment is supported by the very structure of the story: the rape scene itself (71–78) continues over several pages, excruciatingly extended by poignant and poetic flashbacks in italics; the approval of Baba is reduced to one short, prosaic paragraph composed of dull, declarative sentences:

> It happened just the way I'd imagined. I opened the door to the smoky study and stepped in. Baba and Rahim Khan were drinking tea and listening to the news crackling on the radio. Their heads turned. Then a smile played on my father's lips. He opened his arms. I put the kite down and walked into his thick hairy arms. I buried my face in the warm of his chest and wept. Baba held me close to him, rocking back and forth. In his arms, I forgot what I had done. And that was good. (79)

Amir later mentions that both he and Baba immersed themselves in "a sweet illusion," as if "a toy made of tissue paper, glue, and bamboo could somehow close the chasm" between them (87). But even at the time, Amir's sense of guilt outweighs this fragile fantasy. Sitting on the edge of a deserted swimming pool shortly after the kite contest, he muses: "I finally had what I'd wanted all those years. Except now that I had it, I felt as empty as this unkempt pool I was dangling my legs into" (85). As usual, it is Rahim Khan who best articulates what Amir is feeling. As the two of them take a break from Amir's birthday party, Rahim

Khan recalls his own young love for a servant girl, an impossible romance that pitted the two of them against the world. And "in the end, the world always wins" (99).

As it turns out, this personal sense of disillusionment is quickly mirrored in the larger reality of Afghanistan as a whole. Hosseini has explained that one of his first goals in the story was to preserve the experience of an Afghanistan that no longer exists, the one he enjoyed as a child before the coming of the Russians. What he has captured in *The Kite Runner*, however, is not just a lost world, but its loss. When Ali tells the boys that the gunshots in the night are men shooting ducks, it is with a sense of sinking regret that we, as readers, recall the date at the beginning of the second chapter: 1975. We remember that the world we have entered does not exist in some mythic past after all. Perhaps we recall images that we ourselves have seen on television or in newspapers, and we wait for the arrival of Soviet tanks.

By the time Amir returns to Kabul, the glory days of his childhood have evaporated completely. When he returns to his old house, it is no longer a home. Farid tells him, "You won't find kites or kite shops on Jadeh Maywand or anywhere else in Kabul. Those days are over" (246). The children running through the streets with spools of glass string have been replaced by rough men with Kalashnikovs; the kites in the sky have given way to Russian MiGs. The world has won.

Even the more earthbound sport of soccer has fallen, as is evident in the savage cruelty of Assef's halftime slaughter, one of the most gruesome scenes in the novel. Like the heroes in the first part of the novel, Assef, as the villain, is larger than life—as perhaps he must be to truly threaten an Amir surrounded by allies such as Baba and Hassan. Assef is not just bad; he is almost impossibly evil. Lest the reader fail to recognize just how awful he truly is, Hosseini employs that tried and true method for ascribing ultimate villainy: comparisons to Hitler. In the last third of the book, however, we realize that Assef is perhaps not such a far-fetched character after all. Amir's account of the new Kabul ruled by the Taliban is emotionally crushing for the same reason that we are crushed to read accounts of the Holocaust or the gulag: what seems like a fantastic nightmare, the stuff of horror fiction, is not only humanly possible but has really occurred in our own lifetime. Oh, Sohrab.

And yet.

The Kite Runner is not simply a work of raw realism, a dour reminder that you can't go home again. It remains an uplifting story because it is not a documentary or social satire. It is a tale, and like many old tales, *The Kite Runner* proceeds with a genuine moral purpose. Because the novel is not a simple tale, however, there is no single "moral of the story." Instead, Hosseini constructs a constellation of ideas around the themes of lying and telling the truth. In Baba's moral universe, there is only one sin: theft (17). Amir's world is more complicated. He is not as adept as his father at translating all wrongdoing into his own way of thinking, and even within himself he confronts a dismal array of offenses: arrogance, greed, jealousy, deception, even negligent homicide of his mother. But it is deception that dominates the novel, and the story's heavy disillusionment is, to some extent, counterbalanced by Amir's growth into a man of truth.

Deception comes in two forms: outright lying and failure to tell the truth. Amir's deliberate, outright lies are fairly easy to recognize. Most obvious, perhaps, is his ruse involving the stolen money and watch (104). Amir also dabbles in smaller lies, however, such as the time he stops reading the words printed in the book and begins telling Hassan a story he invents on the spot (30). This is actually a double lie, because he is not only inventing his own tale but also deceiving Hassan by pretending to read from the book. The first of these two lies—the storytelling—actually becomes Amir's career.

More insidious than his outright lies, however, are Amir's repeated failures to tell the truth—a more passive and cowardly form of deception at which he truly excels. He fails to report Hassan's rape to those who might see that justice is served, and he even hides his knowledge of the rape from Hassan himself. The middle third of the book, describing Amir's move to America, might be viewed as a prolonged exercise in amnesia, a hiding of past truths even from himself. His life in America—his education, his career, his love for Soraya—is certainly not a lie. But it might be viewed as the absence of the full truth.

Significantly, Hosseini draws on the imagery of absence and emptiness in this period, most obviously in Amir and Soraya's infertility. In a haunting passage, Amir describes the emptiness of his wife's womb as "a living breathing thing" that seeps into their marriage and lies between them as they sleep (189). Amir himself interprets this infertility as punishment for his sins (188). If it is indeed some form of cosmic retribution, it is a punishment that fits the crime: a lack of children for the lack of truth.

Of course, Amir has very realistic reasons for avoiding the truth. The truth hurts. It can even be used as a weapon. Almost as powerful as Assef's brass knuckles are his words to Hassan before raping him, which Amir overhears:

> Have you ever wondered why [Amir] never includes you in games when he has guests? Why he only plays with you when no one else is around? I'll tell you why, Hazara. Because to him, you're nothing but an ugly pet. Something he can play with when he's bored, something

he can kick when he's angry. Don't ever fool yourself and
think you're something more. (72)

When Hassan responds with a feeble protest—"Amir agha and
I are friends"—readers might well recall Amir's earlier confrontation with Assef, where Amir's own thoughts eerily foreshadow
and validate Assef's cutting accusations:

> *But he's not my friend!* I almost blurted. *He's my servant!*
> Had I really thought that? Of course I hadn't. I hadn't. I
> treated Hassan well, just like a friend, better even, more
> like a brother. But if so, then why, when Baba's friends
> came to visit with their kids, didn't I ever include Hassan
> in our games? Why did I play with Hassan only when no
> one else was around? (41)

For all Assef's hyperbole and arrogant self-centeredness, his
insight into Amir is precise and devastating. And surely Hassan,
with his preternatural powers of perception, knows how Amir
really views him. Before Assef assaults Hassan physically, he assaults him—and Amir, as it turns out—emotionally, simply by
telling the terrible truth.

It is important to the story that we hear Amir's unfriendly attitude toward Hassan in his own words before we hear them in
Assef's, because this shows us that, at some level, Amir really
does know the truth about himself. He is not a sociopath, completely lacking a moral sensibility. He knows. Walking home
from viewing the rape, he interprets everything happening in his
heart with ruthless clarity. "I actually *aspired* to cowardice," he
says, "because the real reason I was running, was that Assef was
right: Nothing was free in this world. Maybe Hassan was the
price I had to pay, the lamb I had to slay, to win Baba" (77). Assef
knows Amir well, but Amir knows himself even better.

It is, therefore, not the case that Amir is lost and then found, that he is blind and then he sees. He has always seen. Even in the early parts of the novel, Amir continually makes halfhearted attempts at atonement. He knows he ought to be punished, and at least a part of him even wants to be punished. Recalling the ways he would tease Hassan, he says: "I would always feel guilty about it later. So I'd try to make up for it by giving him one of my old shirts or a broken toy. I would tell myself that was amends enough for a harmless prank" (29). Similarly, winning the kite tournament is supposed to atone for killing his mother, as if a secondhand toy were sufficient restitution for murder.

After Hassan's ordeal in the alley—and Amir's stubborn, sulking silence—Amir's need for atonement becomes even more acute. At one point, he hurls a pomegranate at Hassan in a futile attempt to invite Hassan's righteous retribution: "'Hit me back!' I spat. 'Hit me back, goddamn you!' I wished he would. I wished he'd give me the punishment I craved, so maybe I'd finally sleep at night. Maybe then things could return to how they used to be between us" (92). He knows that he deserves punishment. This desperate sense of personal honesty is also evident as he waits for Assef to enter the room where they will fight. "This isn't you, Amir," a part of him says. "You're gutless. It's how you were made. And that's not such a bad thing because your saving grace is that you've never lied to yourself about it. Not about that" (275).

It is this moral core—this knowledge of truth—that both torments Amir and enables his redemption. If Rahim is correct that redemption is when "guilt leads to good" (302), he is also correct that Amir has the potential to be redeemed. The last third of the novel shows his saving grace becoming real as Amir faces one terrible truth after another. Amir's rescue mission to Assef's compound is at first conducted under false pretenses and, more concretely, a false beard. He accomplishes this mission only after the beard comes off, true identities are revealed all around, and painful truths are confronted square in the face. In the last third of the novel, Amir is most triumphant when he is telling the truth: he candidly tells Wahid and Farid that Hassan was his illegitimate half-brother (237); he confesses his shameful past to Soraya (325); he finally faces down his father-in-law with a direct—almost blunt—account of Sohrab's lineage (361). In all of these instances, Amir accomplishes what even the mighty Baba could not. He tells the full truth.

And just as lies and amnesia give way to truth and memory, so are the absences filled with presence by the end of the story. Running across the hillside to launch a kite for the glum Sohrab, Amir looks down and is surprised to see Sohrab himself running at his side: "I felt a presence next to me and looked down. It was Sohrab. Hands dug deep in the pockets of his raincoat. He had followed me" (368). These are moving lines because Sohrab's physical presence with Amir suggests other forms of presence, as well. He is engaging in the world again. Sohrab is emotionally vacant for most of the book's ending, but in the final pages, Amir sees a hint of a smile: "One corner of his mouth had curled up just so. A smile. Lopsided. Hardly there. But there" (371).

Alongside Amir's movements from deception to truth, from absence to presence, is a religious move. Despite his lessons with the mullahs, and despite the religious practices of Ali and Hassan, we learn that the young Amir "still hadn't made up [his] mind about God" (62). Even when Baba is battling cancer in America, Amir seems not to have decided. He gets out his prayer rug and prays for Baba's health, but he has half forgotten the verses and isn't even sure that there is a God to hear him (154).

It is only in his anguished longing for Sohrab's recovery that he discerns the existence of God (346). What makes this prayer different from the earlier ones, perhaps, is that it begins in confession. Amir prays that God will forgive him for forgetting his faith, and for lying to those who loved him. In other words, Amir's conversion to faith is of a piece with the other redemptive themes of the novel: he acknowledges the presence of God and he tells the bitter truth about his own sins.

Guilt leads to good. Confession invites forgiveness. The language of penitence is dramatically interwoven with words of healing as the doctor interrupts Amir's prayer with the news of Sohrab's recovery:

> *La illaha il Allah, Muhammad u rasul ullah.*
> They had to transfuse several units of red cells—
> *How will I tell Soraya?*
> Twice, they had to revive him—
> *I will do* namaz [prayer], *I will do* zakat [charity].
> They would have lost him if his heart hadn't been
>   young and strong—
> *I will fast.*
> He is alive. (348)

Although the doctor obviously speaks these last three words in reference to Sohrab, they also apply to Amir, whose spiritual revival parallels Sohrab's physical revival.

Near the end of the novel, Amir lets slip a quick clue that his faith has taken root. He mentions that he now knows the prayers by heart and does not need to consult the pamphlet he obtained from the mosque (364), letting the reader know not only that he has been diligent at prayers, but also that he has been to the mosque. That is, his religion seems to have moved from a private plea in a moment of crisis to public and active participation in the community of Islam. In a sense, he has gained a large family that should have been a part of his heritage as an Afghani boy. Amir's conversion to Islam is not a central theme in *The Kite Runner;* rather, it supplements the general moral themes that appear more explicitly throughout the novel. In finding Islam, Amir regains an aspect of his Afghani heritage that was absent from his life even in his glory days in old Kabul.

In order to fly, a kite needs both earth and air. It needs moving air, of course, to lift it into the sky. But it also requires someone on the ground, either standing or running, pulling the line against the wind. If the kite has no wind, it cannot rise; if it is ungrounded, it will not stay aloft for long. The same might be said of *The Kite Runner* as a novel. The book takes magical, mythical themes and plots from old tales and grounds them in personal and historical reality. The happy ending of the story is not, perhaps, as happy as it would be in a fairy tale. History does not return the world it has taken from Amir. Hassan is still dead; there are still no kites over Kabul; Sohrab's own spirits show only the feeble first signs of lifting. But these realities make it even more remarkable that there has been any recovery whatsoever. It is the tension between the ideal and the real that gives the story its loft.

Amir's frantic prayer for Sohrab offers a good example of this tension. His own promises are like downward tugs on a line: he debases himself; he offers to fast; he promises to give money to the poor (zakat). But these tugs are accompanied both by the doctor's news of Sohrab's rising health and, more subtly perhaps, by the reader's recognition that, through truthful contrition, Amir's own soul has risen to the challenge given to him by Rahim Khan. He is good again.

▨ Discussion Questions about the Novel

1. Does guilt lead to good? Think about times in your own life when you have confronted an ugly truth about yourself.

Does this kind of confrontation usually enable the kind of redemption described in *The Kite Runner*? Or does Amir's regeneration seem idealized?

2. Although Amir makes what amends he can by the end of the book, he spends most of the first two-thirds of the story in a kind of sulky selfishness, thriving on the sacrifices of others—Baba, Hassan—and often going so far as to betray these people. What keeps us engaged with such a character?

3. Why does Baba so readily forgive Hassan for stealing the watch (104–5)? As Amir observes, this is a clear violation of Baba's first and last commandment: thou shalt not steal. Even if Baba were somehow to know the truth—that Amir has hidden the watch and is setting Hassan up—would he not then punish Hassan for a fraudulent confession, for stealing Baba's right to the truth?

4. At several points, the novel deals with the importance of blood relationships. General Taheri takes a dim view of adoption because he places so much emphasis on "blood" (87–88). How did you react to his speech? How do you think Amir feels about the issue? He has had an easy life, after all, partly because he carries the blood of his mighty father; but on the other hand, he has been tormented by his failures to live up to that heritage. Does Amir's attitude toward Sohrab change when Rahim Khan reveals that the two are related by blood? The fact that Amir is Sohrab's half-uncle gets him into the orphanage (252), and it is one of the few things that might offer leverage at the embassy (329). Do you think that Amir would have gone to rescue Sohrab had he not turned out to be a blood relation?

5. Amir himself admits that his upbringing with three other males has impoverished his experience of females. Does this seem true of the novel as a whole? All of the major characters, and most of the minor ones, are males. Even Soraya, despite her very human history, seems unimportant to the plot. Amir frequently romanticizes her as a beautiful princess from a fantastic story (140, 191). Does Hosseini also portray her with the gravity and reality that he shows in the other characters?

6. This novel explores several forms of lying, and its plot feels redemptive to most readers precisely because Amir grows into a man who finally confronts and speaks the hard truth. But the novel itself, like all novels, is a piece of fiction—a lovely lie. What distinguishes this form of lying from the lies and suppressions of truth that plague Amir for the first two-thirds of the story?

▨ Other Books to Consider

—Abolqasem Ferdowsi, *Shahnameh: The Persian Book of Kings.* Translated by Dick Davis. New York: Viking, 2006.

> Compiled around 1000 AD, this collection of historical and mythical stories from present-day Iran is widely regarded as the crown jewel of Persian literature. The tragedy *Rostam and Sohrab,* included in the collection, can be read apart from the *Shahnamah* and is often published separately.

—John Irving, *A Prayer for Owen Meany.* New York: Morrow, 1989.

> John Wheelwright, the middle-aged narrator of the novel, reflects on dramatic events from his childhood and adolescence, including the death of a parent, a fast friendship with Owen Meany, wrestling with the Christian faith, and—eventually—the Vietnam War.

—Jhumpa Lahiri, *The Namesake*. Boston: Houghton Mifflin, 2003.

> This novel follows the lives of two generations of Bengali immigrants to the United States, realistically depicting relationships between husbands and wives, parents and children, and Indian and American cultures.

—Naguib Mahfouz, *The Cairo Trilogy*. Translated by William Maynard Hutchins, et al. New York: Alfred A. Knopf, 2001.

> First published in the mid-1950s, these three historical novels (*Palace Walk*, *Palace of Desire*, *Sugar Street*) follow the lives of an Egyptian family from 1917 through 1952. Mahfouz was awarded the Nobel Prize for Literature in 1988.

THE ROAD   Cormac McCarthy
(2006)

A father and son trek among the ghosts of a world that will never be again. A catastrophe ten years earlier began a chain reaction that disrupted every natural cycle and every human invention. Pollination, photosynthesis, the seasons, government, religion, commerce, and society have all vanished. Within the boundaries of their known world, only mushrooms grow. Searching for food, clothing, and shelter and hiding from cannibals—and trekking to the shore—are the sum of their existence.

The monotony of their survival is punctuated by horrific and disturbing encounters. Each day is the same. They awake from their cold sleep to a sunless and gray sky and empty bellies. Warily, they walk the road in rags and wear masks to filter the ash-laden air. At dusk, they seek shelter from the prowling evil ones. If their cover is clever enough, they build a small comforting fire. This meager existence is disrupted only by other survivors bent on diverting them from their journey, while unforgettable horrors remind the father and son just how lost the world is and how isolated they are.

But they are not entirely lost. They have each other and an enduring faith in goodness. A complex relationship develops, in which each supplies meaning to the other's existence. "Each the other's world entire," says McCarthy. The child offers the man a superior moral compass and perhaps redemption and salvation. The man gives the child safety and reassurance. They are on a quest, perhaps

Synopsis

a fool's errand, to remain human and to show the dying world that goodness endures, even if nothing else will.

On the Author

Cormac McCarthy (b. 1933) is a private man, having granted only a few interviews during his career and infused his works with meager autobiographical scraps. One reviewer wryly wrote that "he shunned publicity so effectively that he wasn't even famous for it." He has written fiction, poetry, and plays since 1965, received numerous awards and fellowships, and garnered much critical acclaim. But after nearly three decades of writing in obscurity, *All the Pretty Horses* (1992) propelled McCarthy into the spotlight and established him as a force in American fiction.

A central theme in McCarthy's novels is the force and presence of evil. *Child of God* (1974), *Suttree* (1979), and *Blood Meridian* (1985), three early novels, present central characters that are murderous and depraved. This has earned him a reputation as macabre, graphically violent, and pessimistic. Perhaps it was the relative humanness of the central character of *All the Pretty Horses* that allowed people to finally publicly acknowledge his talents. But his study of evil has persisted in his latest works, including *No Country for Old Men* (2005) and *The Road* (2006). *The Road* diverges from this theme only in that it is also a study in the persistence of good in the face of evil.

Considering the Novel

A profound and heavy absence introduces the story and sets the tone:

> When he woke in the woods in the dark and the cold of the night he'd reach out to touch the child sleeping beside him. Nights dark beyond darkness and the days more

gray each one than what had gone before. Like the onset
of some cold glaucoma dimming away the world. (3)

Dark is the absence of light, gray the absence of color, cold the
absence of heat, and glaucoma the absence of health and sight.
This litany of losses continues throughout the novel. The world
created by humans is gone, names have no relevance, societal
and cultural norms have crumbled, not a speck of civilization
remains. Even the past and the future have ceased to exist. The
natural world fares no better: there are no birds, no trees, no sun-
shine, no crops, no sea creatures. Only negation, dark, cold, and
evil remain in the world. "On this road," the man sighs, "there
are no godspoke men. They are gone and I am left and they have
taken with them the world" (32). If hell is the complete absence
of God and good, as some theologians claim, then the world that
McCarthy paints is hell. It is in this hell we find the man and the
boy, "like pilgrims in a fable swallowed up and lost among the
inward parts of some granitic beast" (3).

Is this a story of unrelenting and universal hopelessness? Has
McCarthy painted himself into a literary corner where all life will
be snuffed out like a smoldering wick? Redemption and salvation,
both spiritual and natural, seem to have gone extinct with the birds
and sea creatures. McCarthy invites us to wander through a mythic
world in which all former categories, assumptions, advancements,
and knowledge are like the grass of the field that withers. What is
important? How do we live? What do we live for? Three responses
play out in *The Road*, three different roads to travel: the mother
chooses annihilation, the cannibals choose evil, and the father and
son choose goodness. The question seems to be not whether the
world will end, but if goodness itself will cease to exist.

The Road is often categorized as a postapocalyptic story. While
it certainly has many characteristics of that genre, it is subtly different. Apocalyptic stories typically carry a strong undercurrent

of moralizing or warning, reflecting on a wrong in the author's world. They warn of the folly of stockpiling nuclear weapons. Or they uncover our smug attitude toward the genetic engineering that will bring humanity to the abyss. Or they preach that invisible microbes will eventually destroy us. But McCarthy does not preach, moralize, or warn. We learn nothing from *The Road* that will make life better or avert an apocalypse.

McCarthy is equally uninterested in the causes of the natural, social, and political meltdown, beyond the trivial fact that it began "at 1:17" (52). We are not privy to the decline of the United States or how civilization unraveled. It is not even important to know when the story takes place. We don't know if the journey occurs in the near or far future. The desolated world merely serves as a black backdrop, allowing us to focus intensely on the thoughts and decisions of the main characters; nothing else about the catastrophe matters.

Instead of thinking of *The Road* as a postapocalyptic story, it may be helpful to consider the novel as a quest narrative, as the title suggests. Quest narratives contain several common elements that provide structure and meaning to the travail of the protagonist. The quest takes place during a time of upheaval and chaos, and the place and time are not essential for the story. The person undertaking the journey is a hero who endures terrible hardship and encounters ghosts, seers, tempters, and monsters along the way. There is a sacred or precious object that is either sought or protected.

The man in this quest narrative is an unlikely hero. He hides or runs away and does shameful and stupid things. He leaves a man to die, refuses food to starving travelers, and allows prisoners to be eaten piecemeal. Against common sense, he puts his son in harm's way. His son often has to make him change his mind and do good things. But he is a hero because he perseveres nobly and strives after goodness. In a world where parents eat their children, he hugs his son and tells him stories of courage and justice. In a world where murder is the norm, he won't even kill and eat a dog. He selflessly endangers himself for the sake of his child. Freezing feet, fatigue, hunger, sunless sky, and terror do not extinguish his humanity or goodness. His is a fortitude few have needed to muster.

He chooses to love and protect his son, even when his wife leaves him. "My job is to take care of you," he says to the boy, "I was appointed to do that by God" (77). The man is always touching, hugging, or kissing the boy. He speaks kindly to him. An intimate scene at the beginning of the novel, emphasizing trust, companionship, and love, is a template for their relationship until the end:

> Then he opened his eyes. Hi, Papa, he said.
> I'm right here.
> I know. . . .
> Then they set out along the blacktop in the gunmetal light, shuffling through the ash, each the other's world entire. (5–6)

Is it love for the boy or fear of death that motives the man's tenderness? Initially, it may be fear. The father confesses that the boy is his "warrant" and that his son is all that stands between him and death (5). Then, too, his fealty is motivated by a desire to prove his wife wrong. Her last cutting words, "Maybe you'll be good at this. I doubt it, but who knows," stay with him for years (57). The relationship between the father and son is complex, but clearly a deep love develops between the two. At the beginning, the man could entertain the possibility of a murder-suicide, but later, when capture by the cannibals is almost certain, he cannot kill his son. In anguish, he wonders, "Could you crush that beloved skull with a rock? Is there such a being within you of which you know nothing? . . . Pull him toward you. Kiss him. Quickly" (114). In the relentless negation of their world, his love for his son is a weighty and heroic thing.

Often heroism is about doing ordinary things, knowing those actions are doomed or will inevitably lead to suffering and sacrifice. "What's the bravest thing you ever did?" the boy asks his father. "Getting up this morning," is his reply (272). He stoically accepts his duty, does it well, and in the end accomplishes his mission of keeping his son safe and arriving at the sea. But there is a part of him that wants to give up, not to shoulder this heavy burden. After discovering the food cache in the bomb shelter, "some part of him wished they'd never found this refuge. Some part of him always wished it to be over" (154). Later we are told that "there were few nights lying in the dark that he did not envy the dead" (230). He inspires his son with stories of the "fire inside" and of being the "good guys," but the reader is unsure if he really believes those stories. McCarthy comments "that he could not enkindle in the heart of the child what was ashes in his own" (154).

Early in the story, the man is presented with a reasonable alternative to his choice of pursuing goodness. The boy's mother coldly and rationally chooses another road. "As for me my only hope is for eternal nothingness and I hope it with all my heart" (57), she says just before she wanders off into the darkness with a flake of razor-sharp obsidian. "And she was right," the man thinks. "There was no argument" (58). Hers was not an irrational choice. Yet he chooses the noble and tragic middle road of suffering. He renounces both suicide and cannibalism because they both eliminate the possibility of goodness.

The boy himself is portrayed as someone special, perhaps a sacred object. He is a new creature, variously described as "the word of God" (5), loved by God, and a believer in God (174). The father refers to him as his "golden chalice" (75), possibly a reference to the Last Supper or the Holy Grail. Near death, the man sees his son down the road "looking back at him from some unimaginable future, glowing in that waste like a tabernacle" (273). Encountering Ely, the nearly blind wanderer, on the road, the boy pleads with his father to give him food. Reluctantly, the father gives the boy a can of fruit cocktail. In a fashion reminiscent of the Last Supper, the boy says to Ely, "Take it . . . Eat it" (163–64).

The boy does not appear to be plagued by any of the sins of the pre-apocalyptic world. As the father reminisces in his boyhood home, "the boy watched him. Watched shapes claiming him he could not see" (26). The vanity, the fatalism, the materialism, and all the other dead philosophies of the prior age have no effect on the boy. There are only two times that the boy has no empathy or compassion for people—after his mother's suicide and after Ely preaches his philosophy of fatalism. "She's gone isn't she?" the boy asked the morning after his mother's death (58). And that was all he said or did. It is as if in rejecting her fatalism, he must also reject her. Similarly, when Ely leaves after a lengthy and meandering diatribe about the meaninglessness of existence, the father watches Ely "dwindling slowly on the road behind them . . . dark and bent and spider thin," but "the boy never looked back at all" (174). Was there something in Ely's discourse on existence and God that caused the boy to reject him? When Ely sarcastically predicts that the boy will "get over" his belief in God, the father confidently replies, "No he wont" (174).

Their encounter with Ely presents enticing philosophical musings. Like the Sirens of the Odyssey, Ely appears to be a tempter seeking to divert the man from his quest. Ely is a materialist, believing in nothing but what can be seen or touched. Like the boy's dead mother, he invites the man to entertain the possibility that death simply ends in annihilation, that there is nothing beyond the grave. However, Ely's philosophy is even more enticing. When you die, he argues, everything ceases to exist. A person does not have to worry about leaving loved ones behind or missing out on life because those things also cease after death. Even more appealing, the dying, rotten earth will disappear at death. Asked how he would know if he were the last man on earth, Ely replies, "It wouldn't make any difference. When you die it's the same as if everyone else did too" (170). When the world dies, so does God. As Ely says, "Where men cant live gods fare no better" (172). How tempting for the father to believe that the unrelenting horrors they have experienced for nearly a decade are simply a nightmare that will end with a well-placed bullet.

Yet the son dismisses Ely and his arguments. Is he morally superior to his father? His father is so consumed with the task of survival that he often forgets to act morally. The boy, on the other hand, is mature beyond his years and often helps his father make right choices. In the bomb shelter, he prays to the dead providers: "We know that you saved [the food] for yourself and if you were here we wouldnt eat it no matter how hungry we were" (146). After taking gear and provisions from the grounded boat, the man must convince his son the owners are dead. "Because if they were alive we'd be taking their stuff" (243), the boy reasons. We see the moral self-awareness of the boy when he berates his father for leaving the thief on the coast in a situation where he will surely die. The father retorts, "You're not the one who has to worry about everything." "Yes I am. . . . I am the one," the boy quietly responds (259). Later, to justify his actions, the father says, "I wasnt going to kill him." To which the son answers, "But we did kill him" (260). Selfless compassion is an essential trait of the boy. Whether it is a dog, a child, or an old wanderer, he wants to share what they have or take the lonely traveler with them. Many months after their encounter with the lone boy, the son is still worried about his well-being (280). Yet despite this moral maturity, his signature response, "Okay," reflects his trust in his father. Whether the son is morally superior to the father is an unresolved question. Clearly, though, the father gives his son room to exercise high moral judgment by taking on the tasks of survival and protection.

At another level, the son can be viewed as his father's savior. The novel begins with the man dreaming. The pair is wandering through a cave with "deep stone flues where the water dripped and sang. Tolling in the silence the minutes of the earth and the hours and the days of it and the years without cease" (3). This same imagery appears again at the end in the man's death delirium. In the first dream, "the child led him by the hand" (3). In the last dream, "the light was a candle which the boy bore" (280). Significantly, the boy carries the candle—the fire—and leads the man. The man may have been providing material comforts and protection, but it is the boy who is guiding and leading the quest. He is providing the moral compass. Early on, the father is correct when he declares that the boy is his warrant. But the father envisions him as a warrant—a guarantee—to protect him from death. In reality, the boy is his authorization and justification—another meaning of *warrant*—to do and seek goodness. It is difficult to discover McCarthy's intent in the bare prose. The man's warrant could refer to nothing more than the "passing of the torch" from one generation to the next. Or perhaps the child himself is the embodiment of innocence and purity, a new creature rising, phoenix-like, from the ashes of the ancient world, and thus a warrant for goodness.

A quest narrative is not complete without ghosts, monsters, and tempters thwarting the weary travelers. Ghosts of the past haunt the man. Hardly a day goes by that a common object of the extinct world—the last swig of Coke, the useless wallet, the sign for Rock City—does not send the man into reverie or despair. Standing in his boyhood home, he thinks of Christmas. Charred corpses and rusting vehicles remind him of bustling cities and the comforts of civilization. Yet he knows full well that "the last instance of a thing takes the class with it" (28) and that only bad dreams remain. The ghosts remind him of how much he has lost. From the boy's perspective, the vestiges of the former age are only havens for monsters. Buildings terrify him. The flesh and blood waiting behind a door to kill and eat him is what he fears, not the dead things of the past.

McCarthy serves up memorable monsters and many indelible images of horror and evil. His monsters are especially horrific because they used to be humans and are now manifestations of the other road the man could have traveled. The first human he speaks to in over a year is described as having "reptilian calculations in those cold and shifting eyes. The gray and rotting teeth. Claggy with human flesh" (75). The child on a spit is an image of absolute evil. The description of the marauding band with its retinue of human livestock, pregnant women, and catamites is chilling in what it leaves to the imagination. There is no hint of possible redemption. Not only has there been a complete breakdown of natural and human systems, but matters of the spirit have also become nearly extinct.

Yet in spite of ghosts, monsters, and tempters, the pilgrims wearily continue their journey to the southern sea. For what is the father questing? He is seeking a safe place for his son. He knows he is dying—he has begun to cough up blood—and he desperately wants to entrust his son to others who have the fire inside. After years of hiding and avoiding the monsters, he fires a flare gun, announcing their location to everyone for miles around.

But he also seeks something more, something transcendent. Like his son, he believes there is more to living than what is taught in the philosophies of his wife or Ely, or what is practiced in the barbarism of the cannibals. As the man lies dying, his last words are a statement of faith, almost a creed. Addressing his son's concern for the small boy they left behind, he says, "Goodness will find the little boy. It always has. It will again" (281). After an unrelenting journey through the abyss of nothingness, this is a startling statement. When all vestiges of religion, holiness, and deity have disappeared, when humanity's very connection to the sacred appears to be permanently severed, he believes in goodness—a goodness that exists beyond material and human existence. This is his belated response to Ely. He believes, still, in something outside the material world—something that exists even if humanity ceases to exist.

Is the goodness he seeks God? He invokes God's name frequently. Referring to his son, he says, "If he is not the word of God God never spoke" (5). Later he rails at God and asks, "Have you a neck by which to throttle you?" (11–12). Contemplating killing his son, he thinks that, reminiscent of Job's wife, he will "curse God and die" and get the terrible deed over with. But is McCarthy's God personal or simply an impersonal force? Is he the hum of mystery that is "older than man" (287)?

The father clings to the reality of goodness in spite of his wife's enticing choice, the tempter's philosophy, and the futility of the situation. We come to realize that his response, "We're the good guys," and his frequent mention of the "fire inside" are not platitudes used to comfort his son. All along, he is declaring his faith in goodness, even when, perhaps, he cannot articulate that faith. Being the good guys means something to the man and is a reminder of what he is seeking. The man is determined to go down fighting on the right side: "This is what the good guys do. They keep trying. They dont give up," he explains to his son (137).

That goodness, in the form of a benevolent man and his wife, finds his little boy in the end probably would not have surprised the father. But some readers of McCarthy take exception to this ending. McCarthy, they argue, does not do happy endings, so perhaps the story is more ambiguous. The father may have been on a fool's errand all along. He delivers his child safely into the hands of goodness, that is true, but the world may still cease to exist. Perhaps the son is only a "sad and solitary changeling child announcing the arrival of a traveling spectacle . . . who does not know that behind him the players have all been carried off by wolves" (78).

McCarthy allows the possibility that all life may end. He has so completely damaged the cycles of life that neither time nor ingenuity may be able to restart the biotic engine. This slide toward total extinction, "the ponderous counterspectacle of things ceasing to be" (274), is graphically described when McCarthy writes, "The names of birds. Things to eat. Finally the names of things one believed to be true. More fragile than he would have thought. How much was gone already? The sacred idiom shorn of its referents and so of its reality. Drawing down like something trying to preserve heat. In time to wink out forever" (89). We follow the pair as they make their way to the sea, the mother of life, and cling to the hope that global death will be avoided. But the womb of life is dead. Imagining "the cold relentless circling of the intestate earth" and the "crushing black vacuum of the universe" (130) is chilling. Many science fiction and apocalyptic stories have chronicled the near extinction of civilization or humanity, but few have left the reader so shorn of hope.

Is this a novel of unrelenting and universal hopelessness? We end with the question that began this essay. McCarthy seems to be saying that there is hope if one believes there exists something called goodness, something that defines us as humans beyond a

pulse, respiration, and thought. By stripping away every other dis-
traction, he allows simple actions to shine as bright searchlights
on this goodness. The "commune" man buries the boy's father
"as the man had promised" (286). In this simple gesture of kindness and faithfulness, we see morality and goodness. The woman,
too, "would talk to him sometimes about God" (286). In spite
of the hellish conditions, the woman testifies that the "breath of
God . . . pass[es] from man to man through all of time" (286).
The trivial action of the thief on the beach near the end of the
story, hiding the hand with missing digits behind his back, also
hints at the persistence of goodness. His mutilated hand, evidence
of justice meted out in the past, testifies that this was not the first
time he had stolen. Perhaps he had even been banished from his
community for his criminal acts. Hiding his hand exhibits a trait
seldom seen in the story—guilt. Guilt is possible only when there
is a belief in goodness. The sense of right and wrong, the rule of
law, a belief in God will continue, McCarthy seems to be saying.
They are permanent fixtures in the drama called life. And *The
Road* hints at the courage and faith needed to choose that goodness in the face of evil.

▪ Discussion Questions about the Novel

1. People of faith believe that humans are special, that there
   exists a unique relationship between them and God.
   McCarthy posits the possibility that humans will become
   extinct. Is human extinction a possibility if you also believe
   in God?

2. The last paragraph is full of color, texture, and life, and it is
   also absolutely enigmatic. Is it an epitaph for "things which
   could not be put back" (287)? Is it related to the preceding

paragraph, in which the woman talks about the "breath of God?" Is the mystery that hums a hint of some life force that McCarthy believes will recreate life? Do you find hope in this last paragraph?

3. Ely, the nearly blind wanderer, is the only person identified by name. And Ely alludes to the fact that his name may be a pseudonym. Upon the death of the father, however, McCarthy writes that the son "said his name over and over again" (281). Why do you think McCarthy chose to make all his characters nameless? Is his son repeating his father's given name, or is he saying "Father," over and over again? What is the significance of the son repeating the father's name at his deathbed?

4. McCarthy dedicated *The Road* to his son, who is nearly the same age as the boy in the novel. One member of the Emmaus Readers described this as "creepy." What do you think?

5. What is the source of goodness in this novel, and how did the boy acquire his heightened moral character? Can such morality and goodness be completely impersonal?

6. Does the father believe that by handing his son off to people who have the fire inside he is contributing to the continuity of the human race? Or is he simply going through the motions for the sake of his child?

Other Books to Consider

—John Bunyan, *The Pilgrim's Progress*. London: N. Ponder, 1678.

Overcoming trials, temptations, and dangers, Christian travels a path that eventually leads him to the Celestial City.

—Albert Camus, *The Plague*. Translated by Stuart Gilbert. New York: Alfred A. Knopf, 1948.

When the Algerian city of Oran is quarantined because of the plague, the characters choose methods of survival that suggest their own sense of meaning and inevitability.

—William Golding, *Lord of the Flies*. New York: G.P. Putman's Sons, 1954.

A classic study of human nature divorced from accountability.

—Nevil Shute, *On the Beach*. New York: William Morrow, 1957.

Like the survivors in *The Road*, humanity faces extinction. Shute examines the last days and final choices of the survivors.

THE TALE OF
DESPEREAUX   Kate DiCamillo
(2003)

Despereaux Tilling is born the runt of his litter, a tiny mouse
with enormous ears and his eyes oddly open to the light.
Growing up in the walls of the king's castle, he shows no
interest in the scurrying ways of his mouse family. Drawn
to both light and music, he encounters the Princess Pea, to
whom he immediately pledges his honor. But such contact
between mouse and maiden is forbidden, and the Mouse
Council casts Despereaux down into the rat-infested
dungeon. The second book of the novel turns to Roscuro, a
rat born in the dungeon. Roscuro is also drawn to the light
and ventures upstairs. He falls, however, from a chandelier
into the queen's soup, provoking her death, Pea's anger, and a
kingly command outlawing soup, spoons, and rats. Roscuro
returns, brokenhearted, to the dungeon, determined to take
his revenge against Pea. In the third book, the narrator
tells the story of Miggery Sow, a peasant girl who loses her
mother only to have her father sell her to an abusive owner.
Once freed from slavery, she works at the castle as a servant
and meets Roscuro. With the promise that she will become a
princess, the rat convinces Miggery to bring Pea down to the
dungeon at knifepoint. The fourth book ties the stories together, as Despereaux escapes upstairs and takes on the quest
of freeing Pea. Unable to obtain the king's help, Despereaux
returns to the dungeon alone, armed with a needle and forti-
fied by the queen's favorite soup.

Synopsis

Kate DiCamillo was born in Philadelphia in 1964. After she contracted pneumonia, a doctor advised that she move to a warmer climate. Her mother took Kate and her brother to Florida in 1969—her father did not follow the family. At the University of Central Florida, DiCamillo completed a BA in English. She took on a variety of odd jobs, all the while dreaming of becoming a writer. In 1994 she moved to Minnesota and got a job working in the children's literature floor of a book warehouse. Upon reading Christopher Paul Curtis's *The Watsons Go to Birmingham—1963,* she decided to focus on children's literature and wrote *Because of Winn Dixie,* a novel set in Florida about a young girl, her single-parent father, and a smiling stray dog. Published by Candlewick Press in 2000, *Because of Winn Dixie* was named a Newbery Honor Book. In 2001 she published *The Tiger Rising* (a National Book Award finalist), a second novel set in Florida, with a young boy, his single-parent father, and a caged tiger as the central characters.

When asked by a friend's son to write a story about "an unlikely hero" and "one with exceptionally large ears," DiCamillo wrote *The Tale of Despereaux*, which was published in 2003 and won the Newbery Medal. DiCamillo's most recent books include *The Miraculous Journey of Edward Tulane* (2006), a novel describing the trials of a vain china rabbit, chapter books starring a pig named Mercy Watson (2005–2008), and *Great Joy* (2007), a Christmas picture book. *Because of Winn Dixie* was released as a movie in 2005, and an animated version of *The Tale of Despereaux* opened in 2008.

Considering the Novel

The full title of this book is a long one: *The Tale of Despereaux: being the story of a mouse, a princess, some soup, and a spool of thread.* Such a wordy title harkens back to books published in previous centuries, as does the hand-cut appearance of the book's edges. Sections of the novel are not labeled with "Part One," and the like, but with the antique-sounding "Book the First" (9). The story itself has all the fixtures of a traditional fable or fairy tale: talking animals, a royal family, a castle, a cook, a servant girl, and the most striking of all, a narrator who speaks directly to the reader. At the very beginning of the novel, the narrator demands the reader's complete confidence:

> The world is dark, and light is precious.
> Come closer, dear reader.
> You must trust me.
> I am telling you a story. (7)

These lines build the framework for the novel, in which mistrust reins and evil threatens to overcome good completely. The "light" is that of a good story, where heroism shows itself in the lowliest of creatures, a story in which the most unlikely friends discover forgiveness, joy, and hope.

The novel's message may be serious, but the overall tone is playful. More of a wise and amusing relative than a cold, all-knowing presence, the narrator challenges the "dear reader" to look up words in the dictionary or consider an "unsavory truth" (111). While "Book the First" may sound archaic, the actual title of the section, "A Mouse Is Born," sounds at once biblical and contemporary (9). At times the characters sound as if they are imitating characters from *My Fair Lady*—saying "cripes" and "gor." On other occasions, the language is very colloquial: "All that forgiveness and goodness. Blech" (265), or "Zip. Zero.

Nada. Goose eggs" (223, 245). References to 1970s popular culture also abound (the songs "Deep Purple" and "Blinded by Light," for example [30, 85]). Added to this mix is challenging vocabulary ("perfidy," "empathy," "egregious," "aspirations," "comeuppance").

In addition to using a broad range of vocabulary and cultural references, the novel creates humor through its comic presentation of tragedy. The first chapter begins with the Tillings, who have lost all of their litter except for a runt. Antoinette Tilling, a French mouse, complains, "All of that work for nothing." She moans: "It is such the disappointment" and "such the tragedy," before clamoring for her makeup bag (11–12). The approximate English turns the tragedy into a comic commentary on bad parenting. And while Antoinette gives her son a name based on despair and her husband Lester predicts a short life, Despereaux appears as a large-eared, cutely clownish figure, a verbal depiction reinforced by Timothy Basil Ering's delightful drawing (14). At this point, the narrator contradicts Lester's prediction of Despereaux's premature death: "But, reader, he did live. This is his story" (15). Along with the comedy, the narrator reassures us that someone controls the story and can point to a happy ending.

Before that ending arrives, Despereaux faces many trials, particularly in his own community. First of all, he is frail, feverish, and prone to fainting, a handkerchief "at all times" in one paw (17). Despereaux doesn't catch on to "the ways of being a mouse," starting with "the art of scurrying" (20). In a marvelous inversion of the question, "Are you a man or a mouse?" his brother Furlough cries out, "Move! You're a mouse, not a man" (21). But Despereaux is not a "good mouse." When instructed by his sister Merlot to eat a book, he reads it and lingers over the words "once upon a time" and a tale of a knight saving a maiden (24). Despereaux follows ways of walking and thinking that do not make sense to (or rhyme with) Merlot and Furlough. Here the narrator warns that such behavior is dangerous in a castle with a rat-filled dungeon: "Reader, you must know that an interesting fate (sometimes involving rats, sometimes not) awaits almost everyone, mouse or man, who does not conform" (25).

Despereaux's fate is social exclusion, by both mouse and man. His immediate love for music draws him to the sound of singing, and he breaks "the most basic and elemental of all mice rules," revealing himself to the king and the Princess Pea (27). He then breaks "the last of the great, ancient rules of mice" and speaks to Pea (39). The king responds immediately in anger to defend the man-over-mouse world order:

> Rodents do not speak to princesses. We will not have this becoming a topsy-turvy, wrong-headed world. There are rules. Scat. Get lost, before my common sense returns and I have you killed. (40)

Upon hearing of his son's actions, Lester declares, "Mice must act like mice or else there is bound to be trouble" (35). With an ominous tribal rhythm, he beats a drum to call the Mouse Council to try his own son. Furlough will lead his brother Despereaux—the scapemouse—off to the dungeon as family bonds break to uphold the social structure.

In fact, the king and the Mouse Council control parallel societies, based on fear. The Most Very Honored Head Mouse judges that Despereaux "endangers" the entire mouse community because "humans cannot be trusted" (43). According to the king, "rodents know nothing of honor" (41). Since mice and humans can have no confidence in each other, the Mouse Council has "no choice" but to send Despereaux "to the rats" (44). Despereaux breaks his community's rules unconsciously, a rebel with an unknown cause, who totally misses "the point of being a mouse" (49). During his trial, Despereaux finally wakes up to defend himself: "But . . . I broke the rules for good reasons. Because of music. And because of love" (54). In other words, there is more to life than scurrying around for food, and there is much to be gained by meeting those unlike ourselves.

If Lester and Antoinette are less than model parents, other authority figures appear as even greater fools. The Most Very Honored Head Mouse represents, by his very name, vanity capitalized. He oversees the trial with rigor: "We will act civilized" (52). He upholds mouse civilization, however, by sacrificing one of its own through an elaborate execution ritual, one that has littered the dungeon's floor with mice bones and red thread (78, 247). The queen is a "simple soul and always, her whole life, had done nothing except state the overly obvious"—and dies by noting a rat has fallen in her soup (112). In the Kingdom of Dor (from the French *d'or*, "of gold"), the king is not terribly bright and decides to outlaw soup, soup-related implements, and even rats. The narrator jumps in to ask:

> How can you outlaw an outlaw? It is a waste of time and energy. But still, the king officially decreed that all rats in the Kingdom of Dor were outlaws and should be treated as such. When you are a king, you may make as many ridiculous laws as you like. That is what being a king is all about. (119)

Even when offered the chance to redeem himself and help Despereaux free Pea, the king covers his ears and refuses to hear the truth: "There are no rats in my kingdom. They do not exist" (213). He creates his own rat-free reality, unaware of his own rat-like selfishness.

Ironically, the rat Chiaroscuro, long for Roscuro, provides a more complex character than the king. Like his name, Chiaroscuro/Roscuro represents "the arrangement of light and dark, darkness and light together" (85). While "born into the filth and darkness of the dungeon" (85), Roscuro develops "an abnormal, inordinate interest in illumination of all sorts" after Gregory, the dungeon keeper, lights a match in (and to) his face. The punishment has the opposite effect on this "black-souled thing" of a rat: "His rat soul longed inexplicably for it; he began to think that light was the only thing that gave life meaning" (88). Despite his evil nature, Roscuro's attraction to the light and Pea equals that of the mild-mannered Despereaux. They may live in opposing, upstairs-downstairs, French vs. Italian worlds, but the two rodents are "light-bedazzled" (103) and share parallel desires for some greater meaning in their lives.

While Despereaux has to decide between the fine art of scurrying and the fine arts, Roscuro faces a much grimmer choice. In terms of nurture, his rat mentor is the diabolical Botticelli Remorso, always ready to sway a hypnotizing locket before a listener's eyes. Although named after the grand Renaissance painter, Botticelli gives to Roscuro the darkest portrait of life—its meaning is "suffering, specifically the suffering of others" (88). Roscuro is to offer prisoners hope, friendship, whatever their hearts desire, and then take that away (89). The final touch, Botticelli suggests, is to show no remorse, and "run back and forth over the prisoner's feet, inducing physical terror along with the emotional sort" (90). What makes Botticelli even crueler is that he finds this all "a lovely game" whereby evil and suffering create "a lovely, dark world" (90–91). Botticelli plumbs the lowest level of evil, the sadistic pleasure found in torturing others.

Roscuro initially takes Botticelli's advice and steals a red tablecloth from a prisoner. But the suffering Roscuro causes does not provide the pleasure Botticelli predicted: "What Roscuro wanted, what he needed, was not the cloth, but the light that had shone behind it" (102). He goes upstairs, invites himself to the king's party, and is delighted by the spectacle of laughing, happy royals. When banished to the dungeon by Pea's glare, Roscuro resigns himself to being a rat, but an ambitious one. He crowns himself with the queen's soup spoon: "I will have something beautiful. I will have a crown of my own" (114). Upon hearing Miggery Sow, a servant girl, say she wants to become Princess Pea (159), Roscuro tells her, "We two are perfectly suited, each to the other"—because they share the same royal "aspirations" (169–70). Down in the dungeon, Miggery finally puts on Pea's crown, but it doesn't fit and hurts her already sore ears. Revealing his treachery, Roscuro says she looks "ridiculous" and "laughable" (252). Ironically, he looks just as ridiculous with a spoon on his head. Only when Despereaux arrives does Roscuro realize his folly: "It will never work. All I wanted was some light. That is why I brought the princess here, really, just for some beauty . . . some light of my own" (263). Miggery and Roscuro confuse the Pea's beauty and splendor with her inner light, as if it's something they can either steal or control.

The dungeon may be "the dark heart of the world," yet that heart beats not in rats alone (77). Humans fear the dungeon. "Certainly it was never far from their thoughts," says the narrator (154). Is this the fear of "despair and suffering and hopelessness," in other words, depression (73)? Or the fear of becoming a rat, of turning evil? Even the seemingly perfect Princess Pea has a heart that is "complicated, shaded with dark and dappled with light" (197). In Pea's case, the darkness comes through Roscuro. When he falls into her mother's soup bowl, provoking her death, Pea acquires "a tremendous sorrow" and a "hot, burning coal of hatred for the rat" (198). She feels inside herself at once the darkness of depression and the dark desire to take revenge.

As with Despereaux and Roscuro, and Roscuro and Miggery Sow, DiCamillo contrasts Miggery Sow and the princess, another pair of similar but opposing characters, to illustrate the conflict between darkness and light. Both girls lose their mothers, but their childhoods are completely different. Miggery's father sells her into slavery and abuse, while Pea still enjoys her father's riches and music. Pea is sharp eyed and sharp witted (28–29); Miggery's hearing is dull, and she is by no means the "sharpest knife in the drawer" (152). In size and manners, the piggish Sow also offers the perfect foil to the sparkling princess. Seeing Pea ride by with her parents, Miggery is struck by "the brilliant light" of their apparel and crowns (132), which she wants to possess (137, 150–51). In contrast to Miggery's superficial view of "light," Pea learns to control her inner darkness. When Miggery and Roscuro break into her room, Pea "stared at the rat," boldly facing her fear and anger (193). More important, as Miggery forces her to the dungeon, Pea manages to feel empathy for the misguided servant girl (198). In the dungeon, the princess realizes there must be some reason behind Miggery's actions and asks what her abductor craves. Miggery's own heart breaks as she admits that, like Pea, she just wants her "ma" back (254). Miggery then turns to her side and offers to kill Roscuro. But "suddenly aware how fragile her heart was, how much darkness was inside it, fighting always with the light," the princess stops Miggery and forgives Roscuro, "to save her own heart" (264). In her refusal to pay back evil with evil, Pea provides the light of forgiveness and healing.

Various episodes in the novel present the conflict between light and dark through religious terms. For example, Roscuro encourages the prisoner to confess his sins (99), of which the tablecloth is a reminder (101). The Mouse Council will make Despereaux "hear of his sins" so "he may go to the dungeon with a pure heart" (44–45). During his trial, he is asked to "renounce" his actions and "repent" in the manner of a medieval heretic (55), with the crowd yelling, "To the dungeon. To the dungeon. To the dungeon" (56). Despereaux goes down to his death, returns to life, but remains unsure of how to save Pea. All alone, hiding in the kitchen, "the mouse wept" (181). Anointed with oil and clothed in white flour, he then appears before the Mouse Council and calls on them to repent. Back in the dungeon, Despereaux— now the savior mouse—faces the devilish Botticelli, takes hold of him by the tail (246) and then places a needle to the heart of Roscuro, the would-be king of darkness and light (171, 260).

DiCamillo points to more than the Bible in her writing. The story openly imitates the literary tradition of the courtly romance, of the knight heading off on a "quest" to save a fair maiden from a captor (221). If Despereaux saves Pea, it is as a "knight with a shining needle" (265), motivated by love and armed against hatred and evil. And so, on the one paw, we have Botticelli informing Roscuro: "A rat is a rat is a rat. End of story. World without end. Amen" (97). Combining Gertrude Stein (think of roses, not rats) and the Book of Common Prayer, Botticelli argues that evil will abide, and so evil is justified. On the other paw, we have Despereaux, who has "been to the dungeon and back up out of it" (208), and can face the injustice of his elders, the selfishness of the king, and the cruelty of a rat. His actions produce good out of love, just as Pea chooses to help Miggery and forgive Roscuro out of empathy. The narrator stresses that "every action, reader, no matter how small, has a consequence" (117). Love may be "ridiculous"—especially that of a mouse for a princess. But such love is both "powerful" and "wonderful," as it defies the logic of selfish self-preservation (32). Choices based on love and respect may be risky, but they bring positive consequences, turning a feeble mouse into a hero, a vain servant girl into a friend, and a rat into an honored dinner guest.

In this realm of good and bad choices, Gregory the dungeon keeper and Hovis the threadmaster stand to the side of, if not above, all other characters. Both occupy questionable positions as the enforcers of cruel and clearly unjust practices. Hovis sends mice to their death, while Gregory keeps mice and prisoners to their death. Yet both question the systems they uphold and are wise to the point of being prophetic. Gregory reveals to Despereaux the piles of outlawed soup implements, "the twisted results of love," "a monument to the foolishness of love," built by the king after the loss of his wife (79). He sees that love, when misdirected, has bad results. He sees the rat dancing in the darkness, dreaming the "foolish dream" that he can control the light he loves (164). Although charged with putting the "red thread of death" around the neck of a dungeon-row mouse, Hovis is no menacing figure. He smells of celery, "green and alive," and offers professorial encouragement by explaining the nature of courtly love to Despereaux (61). When Despereaux later asks for the spool of thread to chart his way through the dungeon, Hovis first hesitates, as he can't just hand over this "sacred" thread. He admits, though, that it is just thread: "But I pretend, friend, I pretend." This free-thinking mouse chomps his celery with "a meditative bite" and finally sends Despereaux on his way, armed with the thread, a needle, and the word *quest* (218).

Even more than the power of love, it is the strength of good storytelling that saves Despereaux from darkness and death. Of course, reading first gets him into trouble with his siblings. But in the dungeon, Gregory saves Despereaux when the mouse is caught saying to himself, "Once upon a time." And the jailer then commands Despereaux: "Stories are light. Light is precious in a world so dark. Begin at the beginning. Tell Gregory a story. Make some light" (81). For a story to provide "light," it need not be lightweight. As the narrator argues about the novel's final section:

> The story is not a pretty one. There is violence in it. And cruelty. But stories that are not pretty have a certain value too, I suppose. Everything as you well know (having lived in this world long enough to have figured out a thing or two for yourself), cannot always be sweetness and light. (183)

The narrator treats child readers like adults, and trusts they can understand the abuse weighed against Miggery's ears, Gregory's terrible death, Botticelli's love for torture, the "grinning skulls and delicate finger bones, rising up of the darkness" in the dungeon, and the taste of soup made of watercress and garlic (247). The novel offers violence with the same directness of a fable or nursery rhyme. In this tale, mouse and rat lose their tails, cut off with a carving knife. But Despereaux soldiers on by making light, by telling himself his own story of courage. In the coda, the narrator again speaks to the reader directly and asks to be seen as Despereaux, a mouse telling a story to escape darkness (270). This may not be the story of faith, but it is the trust that hope and love will overcome, that community is difficult but possible, that king, princess, servant girl, mouse, and rat can sit at the same table and enjoy some soup.

Discussion Questions about the Novel

1. When you read the novel, did you think the narrator was a man or a woman? What would you argue in favor of either gender? Does this affect how you view the story?

2. In the second and third section of the novel, Despereaux disappears as the story focuses on Roscuro and Miggery, along with a number of other interesting characters, such as Botticelli and Miggery's father. In your opinion, how does the entire story—*The Tale of Despereaux*—still hold together?

3. The "clouts" Miggery receives may sound comic, but they are nothing less than child abuse. Botticelli Remorso is a superbly drawn villain, but he proposes torture as a vocation. The descriptive details are often worthy of a horror story, as in Gregory's comments to Despereaux about the rats: "You can hear their tails through the muck and filth. You can hear them filing their nails and teeth. They are coming for you. They are coming to take you apart piece by piece" (78). Does DiCamillo go too far in treating a child reader as an adult?

4. The novel's structure is based on a fair degree of stereotyping. For example, we have fearful French mice and evil Italian rats, as well as a beautiful, slim princess and an unattractive, stout servant girl. How does this stereotyping relate to the novel's themes of individual limitations and personal courage?

5. The narrator claims that a storyteller must be trusted. The rats, however, are marvelous storytellers, with great vocabulary and manners. How can you recognize a trustworthy storyteller?

6. Page through the book and look particularly at the illustrations. How do they support the story? Did you view the characters or setting differently? Are there any passages that should have been illustrated that were not? If you have seen the animated version of *The Tale of Despereaux,* how do film and book compare?

Other Books to Consider

—Richard Adams, *Watership Down*. London: Rex Collings, 1972.

> Under the leadership of Hazel, a group of rabbits leave a comfortable warren to establish a new home at Watership Down. They soon come into contact with the neighboring warren of Efrafra and its despotic leader, the General Woundwort. Battle ensues.

—Brian Jacques, *Redwall*. New York: Philomel Books, 1986.

> Cluny the Scourge, an evil, one-eyed rat, prepares to attack Redwall Abbey. But aided by various animal companions, the mouse Mathias embarks on a quest to find the lost sword of Martin the Warrior and so save Redwall.

—Robert C. O'Brien, *Mrs. Frisby and the Rats of NIMH*. New York: Atheneum, 1971.

> To save her family, a widowed mouse named Mrs. Frisby overcomes her fears and collaborates with the rats of NIMH. This group of highly intelligent rodents, the product of a lab experiment gone awry, will, in turn, depend on Mrs. Frisby to find safety and a new home for themselves.

—E.B. White, *Charlotte's Web*. New York: Harper, 1952.

> Wilbur the pig avoids an early demise thanks to the clever web spinning of a spider named Charlotte. In turn, Wilbur discovers the strengths of community and friendship as he helps to save Charlotte's children.

—E.B. White, *Stuart Little*. New York: Harper, 1945.

> Mrs. Little gives birth to a son who is not much bigger than a mouse. Stuart enjoys life in New York City but must deal with the ill will of Snowbell the cat and a series of adventures that form a quest for his friend, the bird Margalo.

Integrative Discussion Questions for Part Four

1. *The Kite Runner, The Road,* and *The Tale of Despereaux* all contain settings filled with horror, darkness, and despair: the soccer stadium, the road, the dungeon with the rats. Yet sometimes right next to those scenes, or even in their midst, the authors include moments that are achingly tender, generally affirming the love between two beings. How does placing those moments within such darkness affect you as a reader? What do they do to your reading of those tender moments? Does the combination of darkness and tenderness say something about these writers' perceptions of the human condition?

2. Each of these novels makes much of the notion of telling stories. In *The Tale of Despereaux,* Kate DiCamillo insists, in fact, that the storyteller *must* be trusted. Why do we human beings tell stories? Why might we tell these particular stories?

3. Rahim Khan tells Amir that "there is a way to be good again" (2). The father in *The Road* insists that "goodness will find the little boy. It always has. It will again" (281). "Stories are light" (270), Gregory tells Despereaux. How would you describe each of these novel's visions of goodness and light? Do they seem compatible at all? Or are they at odds?

4. Betrayal—of oneself, of another—is prominent in each of these novels and propels characters toward certain responses. Amir's life is determined by his betrayal of Hassan, and Despereaux's father is freed at the end of the novel because

his betrayal has been forgiven. The father in *The Road* never betrays his son, but does occasionally betray the basic instincts of humanity in his drive to protect his son. As they commit acts of betrayal, how do you judge these characters? Does each character receive the same judgment? If not, what have the authors done to lead to differing responses to this, one of the most heinous of sins?

Integrative Discussion Questions about the Novels

1. Is Christianity a Western religion? Or, as historian Andrew Walls has said, is it more accurate to say that the missionaries didn't bring the gospel to Africa, but rather the gospel brought the missionaries to Africa? Certainly it is true in the twenty-first century that there are more Christians outside North America and Europe than reside on those continents. Does Christianity take on the shape of the cultures that it inhabits? Or does it change and deform those cultures? What perspectives do *Fieldwork* and *Purple Hibiscus* offer on these questions?

2. Human selfishness is a large feature both of *Intuition* and *Blindness*. How does the Marxist notion of this malady in *Blindness* differ from Goodman's sense of it in *Intuition*, as formed by her Jewish background? What perspective might McCarthy's *The Road* offer in such a discussion?

3. Although set in radically different contexts, many of the novels in this collection explore the relationship between fathers and sons: for example, *Gilead, The Known World, The Yiddish Policemen's Union, Fieldwork, The Road,* and *The Tale of Despereaux.* What do these novels tell us about fathers and sons? What about the relationship between mothers and sons? Do novels treat these two relationships differently?

4. Several of the novels feature characters who must commit a crime in order to protect a loved one, to save someone from a worse fate, or for the greater good. Are these types

of crimes justified? Do the circumstances or intentions of the perpetrators make a difference? Compare the doctor's wife's murder of the rapist in *Blindness*, Hertz Shemet's murder of Mendel in *The Yiddish Policemen's Union*, and Martiya van der Leun's murder of David Walker in *Fieldwork*.

5. *The Yiddish Policemen's Union*, *The Tale of Despereaux*, and *The Known World* all present characters who are trapped in the "known world" they inhabit and who feel estranged from their surroundings. How do these outsiders find a world to call their own? *Do* they find a world to call their own? What qualities allow certain characters to break free from social conventions and structures?

6. How does Father Amadi in *Purple Hibiscus* compare to Rae in *The Translator*? Each of them, after all, moves easily between multiple cultures; each is respected as an authority figure in at least one of these cultures; each is loved by a younger woman who is clearly out of her element; and in each case, religious vows stand in the way of a lasting romantic relationship. Did you have similar reactions to these two characters?

7. Several novels include graphic violence. In *Purple Hibiscus*, Eugene scalds and pummels his children and wife; in *The Kite Runner*, Assef causes a couple to be stoned at a soccer match; in *March*, Grace is cruelly whipped; in *The Known World*, slaves are mutilated and murdered. Each of these acts of violence occurs in a cultural moment that is somehow remote from the modern American reader. How does that cultural distance affect our reaction to the violence? Do we simply expect life in other times and other places to be more violent?

8. Both *The Road* and *Blindness* deal with apocalyptic visions, but while the world in *The Road* is empty, silent, clean, and dark, in *Blindness* the reader is overwhelmed with the clutter, the smell, and the whiteness. How effective are these very different views of hell?

9. The narrators of *The Tale of Despereaux* and *Blindness* both speak directly to the reader. How does this technique affect the relationship between the reader and the text?

10. *The Translator, Purple Hibiscus,* and *The Kite Runner* are all set in locations that may seem exotic and unfamiliar to North American readers. In what sense do they address universal concerns and to what extent are they tied to particular cultures? Are such "global" novels any more distant than those, like *March* or *The Known World,* that transverse history?

11. In *The Translator, Purple Hibiscus, The Known World, March,* and *The Kite Runner,* characters often feel a deep homesickness, a longing for "place" that transcends other loves and fears. How do the characters in these novels cope with their desire for home? Does it motivate them to goodness? Or does it hinder their emotional, intellectual, or spiritual development?

12. In both *The Road* and *Gilead,* a father attempts the moral education of a young son by telling him stories. In *The Tale of Despereaux,* the narrator insists that stories are light. In what ways are narratives particularly appropriate means of teaching children how to act in the world?

13. *Gilead, The Known World,* and *March* all deal with relationships between blacks and whites in the United States. How are the worlds invoked in these novels similar? Do they all ring true?

14. Compare Amir's conversion to Islam in *The Kite Runner* with the conversion of Rae Isles, the scholar in *The Translator.* What motives or circumstances drive each character to convert, and what effect does religion seem to have on them once they have joined Islam?

15. Rahim Khan and Hassan in *The Kite Runner* would probably both make good detectives. Unlike Baba, they succeed in life not by imposing their intentions on others, but by intuiting what is happening in the hearts and minds of those around them. How does their intuition compare to that of Cliff in *Intuition* and Meyer Landsmann in *The Yiddish Policemen's Union*?

16. Like *Purple Hibiscus, The Kite Runner* stops short of an ideal ending. In *Purple Hibiscus,* Kambili loses the ideal family situation when Ifeoma and her family move to America, where they grow jaded and bitter. In *The Kite Runner,* Sohrab is safe and beginning to adjust, but Amir's own ideal family, the one that included Baba and Hassan, is gone for good. Did you react to the conclusions of these novels in similar ways? How does the failure of these ideals compare to the failure of Mr. March's ideals in *March*?

17. As different as they may be, *The Tale of Despereaux, The Road,* and *Blindness* all present the world as a dark, depressing place. Do they point to a similar "light"?

Acknowledgments

Everything in a book club does go better with good food and good drink. We are grateful to the Calvin Center for Christian Scholarship for a generous grant that provided food and drink—caffeinated, of course—as well as books, time for editing, and the less tangible, but no less appreciated, encouragement that our efforts were worth the investment.

The Emmaus Readers this last year included English professors, a theologian, a librarian, and faculty from the Spanish and French departments. Jennifer Williams, who wrote the essays on *The Known World* and *The Yiddish Policemen's Union,* is an assistant professor of English. She knows something about being a stranger in snowy lands because she and her surfer husband, Dale, are recent transplants to Michigan from Southern California. Cynthia Slagter, who introduced us to José Saramago and who wrote the essay on *Blindness,* teaches Spanish and loves everything connected with the Iberian Peninsula. Otto Selles teaches French and enjoys discussing children's novels and films with his wife and three children; he wrote about *The Tale of Despereaux.* Gary Schmidt, who teaches English and all things New England, delighted in revisiting old Alcott texts as he wrote the essay on *March.* John Rottman, a professor at Calvin Theological Seminary who once thought about becoming a scientist, wrote the essay on *Intuition.* Glenn Remelts, the director of the library at Calvin College and the author of the essay on *The Road,* understands the impulse toward solitude. He tries to avoid people while hiking through the mountains and canyons of the American West. Susan Felch, who teaches English and grew up in Papua New Guinea, enjoyed writing the essays on *Fieldwork, The Translator,* and *Gilead.* Chad Engbers, who teaches world literature, wrote the essays on *Purple Hibiscus* and *The Kite Runner.* He and his wife are in the process of adopting a daughter from Nepal.

We, the editors, have mightily enjoyed sharing our lives with the Emmaus Readers, our little community of conversation and thought. But, as always, we find our center of gravity in Anne Schmidt and Doug Felch. Thank you.

Bibliography

Page numbers in the text refer to the following recent editions of the novels:

—Leila Aboulela, *The Translator* (New York: Black Cat, 1999).

—Chimamanda Ngozi Adichie, *Purple Hibiscus* (New York: Anchor Books, 2004).

—Mischa Berlinski, *Fieldwork* (New York: Farrar, Straus and Giroux, 2007).

—Geraldine Brooks, *March* (New York: Penguin, 2006).

—Michael Chabon, *The Yiddish Policemen's Union* (New York: HarperCollins, 2007).

—Kate DiCamillo, *The Tale of Despereaux* (Cambridge, MA: Candlewick Press, 2006).

—Allegra Goodman, *Intuition* (New York: Dial Press, 2007).

—Khaled Hosseini, *The Kite Runner* (New York: Riverhead Books, 2003).

—Edward P. Jones, *The Known World* (New York: Amistad, 2004).

—Cormac McCarthy, *The Road* (New York: Vintage Books, 2006).

—Marilynne Robinson, *Gilead* (New York: Farrar, Straus and Giroux, 2004).

—José Saramago, *Blindness*. Translated by Giovanni Pontiero. (Orlando, FL: Harvest/Harcourt, 1997).

About Paraclete Press

Who We Are

PARACLETE PRESS is a publisher of books, recordings, and DVDs on Christian spirituality. Our publishing represents a full expression of Christian belief and practice—from Catholic to Evangelical, from Protestant to Orthodox.

We are the publishing arm of the Community of Jesus, an ecumenical monastic community in the Benedictine tradition. As such, we are uniquely positioned in the marketplace without connection to a large corporation and with informal relationships to many branches and denominations of faith.

What We Are Doing

BOOKS | Paraclete publishes books that show the richness and depth of what it means to be Christian. Although Benedictine spirituality is at the heart of all that we do, we publish books that reflect the Christian experience across many cultures, time periods, and houses of worship. We publish books that nourish the vibrant life of the church and its people—books about spiritual practice, formation, history, ideas, and customs.

We have several different series, including the best-selling Living Library, Paraclete Essentials, and Paraclete Giants series of classic texts in contemporary English; A Voice from the Monastery—men and women monastics writing about living a spiritual life today; award-winning literary faith fiction and poetry; and the Active Prayer Series that brings creativity and liveliness to any life of prayer.

RECORDINGS | From Gregorian chant to contemporary American choral works, our music recordings celebrate sacred choral music through the centuries. Paraclete distributes the recordings of the internationally acclaimed choir Gloriæ Dei Cantores, praised for their "rapt and fathomless spiritual intensity" by *American Record Guide*, and the Gloriæ Dei Cantores Schola, which specializes in the study and performance of Gregorian chant. Paraclete is also the exclusive North American distributor of the recordings of the Monastic Choir of St. Peter's Abbey in Solesmes, France, long considered to be a leading authority on Gregorian chant.

DVDS | Our DVDs offer spiritual help, healing, and biblical guidance for life issues: grief and loss, marriage, forgiveness, anger management, facing death, and spiritual formation.

LEARN MORE ABOUT US AT OUR WEB SITE:
www.paracletepress.com, or call us toll-free at 1-800-451-5006.